A HANDBOOK OF
# DYES FROM
# NATURAL MATERIALS

# A HANDBOOK OF
# DYES FROM NATURAL MATERIALS

## Anne Bliss

*Charles Scribner's Sons • New York*

This handbook is respectfully dedicated to the dyers who shared information for this book and to these other of my favorite dyers who have documented and shared "trade secrets" and who have forwarded the ancient and traditional art and craft of dyeing with natural materials:

> *Gioanventura Rosetti, Italy, sixteenth century*
> *Elijah Bemiss, United States of America, eighteenth to nineteenth centuries*
> *William Tucker, United States of America, eighteenth to nineteenth centuries*
> *William Crookes, England, nineteenth century*
> *Erna Bachi-Nussbaumer, Switzerland, twentieth century*
> *Nonabah G. Bryan, United States of America, twentieth century*
> *Mary-Russell Ferrell Colton, United States of America, twentieth century*
> *Mary Frances Davidson, United States of America, twentieth century*
> *Alma Lesch, United States of America, twentieth century*

The yarn pictured on the jacket is commercially spun wool, brushed mohair, loop mohair, and cashmere dyed with cochineal by Linda Berry Walker.

Copyright © 1981 Anne Bliss

Library of Congress Cataloging in Publication Data

Bliss, Anne.
  A handbook of dyes from natural materials.

  Includes index.
1.  Dyes and dyeing, Domestic.   2.   Dye plants.
I.   Title.
TT854.3.B55      667'.26      79-66891
ISBN   0-684-16502-3

1 3 5 7 9 11 13 15 17 19   V/C   20 18 16 14 12 10 8 6 4 2

Printed in the United States of America

Color section printed in Japan

# Acknowledgments

The best part of writing this book has been working with the contributing dyers. Not only have they been willing to share their "trade secrets," but they have imparted to me that genuine feeling of camaraderie known among people who share common insights and goals. Truly they are caretakers of nature and folk artisans in the highest sense. Without them—their ongoing practice of an ancient art and craft and their generous contributions, humor, and encouragement—this book would not exist.

I wish to thank Dr. H. Rex Richards, Dr. Robert Steadman, and Professor Patricia Wilson of the Department of Clothing and Textiles at Colorado State University, with very special thanks to Dr. Steadman for his patience and perseverance with the weatherometer testing.

Imelda DeGraw, Curator of Textiles, and Richard Conn, Curator of Native American Arts at the Denver Art Museum, were most generous with their knowledge and time, and in allowing access to their collections of historic naturally dyed articles.

Linda Ligon at Interweave Press, Inc., has offered good humor, advice, and photographs. Carol Strickler shared her expertise and photographs of early American textiles, particularly handwoven coverlets.

A.B.
*Boulder, Colorado*

# Contents

*Contents*

# Introduction

Any discussion of dyes made from naturally occurring materials necessitates the basic understanding that an individual is using something gathered from nature to impart color. The dyer is extracting color from one material and applying that color to something else, whether it is the dyer's body, a shelter, garments or fabrics, food, or a multitude of other things. Since individual dyers have developed working methods, color and dyestuff sources and preferences, and personal philosophies of dyeing, the results of the color derivation and application tend to be personalized. They are attuned to the dyestuff available to the dyer as well as to the objects to be dyed.

My purpose in writing this book has been threefold:

First, I wanted to examine some basic attitudes and working methods of contemporary dyers in North America who have elected to use natural materials to produce color—a means of dyeing that to many people seems very old-fashioned and silly when there are so many synthetic dyes available for home use.

Second, I wanted to present recipes for natural dyes that have been tested for lightfastness. Many people dismiss natural dyes as fugitive and unfast, and they believe that natural dyes easily lose their color. In fact, just the opposite seems to be true in many cases. To test the dyes, a sample from each method or recipe provided in this book was tested for fastness to light, using industrial methods in a weatherometer. This instrument tests lightfastness by means of a carbon arc lamp in controlled atmospheric conditions. Development of weatherometers came about after synthetic dyes had fairly monopolized the industrial dye market; as a result, most natural dyes have never been tested under the standard industrial methods, nor are there fastness ratings for most natural dyes (these are the ratings used by the dye industry to guide manufacturers in their choice of the proper dye to suit their purposes).

Third, I have been interested in providing natural dyers with a means of communicating about the colors they obtain. Industry uses as a reference the *Colour Index,* which codifies synthetic dyes to a color system that enables the synthetic dyer to actually check on the color that the dye should produce. But only a very few natural dyes are codified in the *Colour Index,* and those are primarily the ones that still have a limited use in the dye industry. Most reference sources for natural dyes give only very general descriptions of the colors produced by the natural materials—for example, "yellow" for goldenrod with alum mordant, or "red" for madder with chrome mordant. To provide a more accurate description, each dyed sample representing the recipes and methods contained in this handbook has been coordinated with the Inter-Society Color Council–National Bureau of Standards (ISCC-NBS) Centroid Colors, and each sample color is designated with the color code for the closest color match to it. The Centroid Color System will be discussed in detail in Chapter 4.

People are often curious about the reasons why I've chosen to dye with natural materials when it would be so much easier to buy a packet of dye powder and have nearly instant color. Perhaps it's because I love soil and plants and my pet cochineal bugs, who slowly suck all the life and color out of the succession of prickly pear cacti I feed them. Perhaps it's because I don't want one of humanity's oldest arts, crafts, and trades to disappear. Perhaps it's because I can wander through the woods or the vacant lots in town, gather up a few unsuspecting plants, take them home, and brew a lovely dye all by myself. Perhaps it's because there are sometimes surprising results in the dyepot that make me wonder and appreciate the fact that I can't always control what nature has produced. Perhaps it's because dyeing with nature feels to me like the way things are meant to be.

I do know that brewing dyes from natural materials has become somewhat of an addiction; I can no longer look at a fruit tree and think only of eating the fruit. Instead, I also think of the color the bark will make when the tree sheds it, or of the color the peelings from some fruit I have eaten will produce. Natural dyeing has become a part of me in a way that adding a packet of laboratory-produced dye powder never could, for working alone with nature is a very personal experience. I enjoy nature's produce, the dye process, the fibers, and the results. I have discovered the rainbow in my dyepot.

PART ONE

# NATURAL DYEING: THE BASICS

# Chapter 1.

# Traditions in Natural Dyeing

No one really knows how or when people first learned that colors could be taken from naturally occurring substances and transferred onto stone, wood, clay, skin, or cloth. Many of the early staining and dyeing discoveries were probably accidental, as when a section of cloth was stained brown as someone sat on iron-rich soil—or perhaps a cook's hands absorbed color from food during its preparation. From dated artifacts and early manuscripts we know that long before the Christian era many civilizations in various parts of the world were using dyes and pigments for many purposes. We also know, for example, that by 3000 B.C. dye workshops were functioning in the Far East. For how many thousands of years had people been dyeing before organizing those workshops? No one knows.

There were several important dyestuffs of antiquity, some of which are still used (though not extensively) in the dye industry. Other dyestuffs have been lost to time, or their processing methods are no longer known. The Tyrian purples and crimsons produced in the Mediterranean area were obtained through a vat-putrefaction process using *Buccinum* or porphyry whelks or mollusks. They were sometimes used in combination with seaweed, and the colors produced were, by law, to be worn only by the highest dignitaries. The dyeing of this purple cloth was practiced somewhat secretively, and it was done exclusively by government-appointed dyers.

Indigo, another vat-process dye, is thought to have been developed in the Far East, involving the derivation of blue color by a process of

3

dyeing and successive oxidation. Indigo vats were prepared directly from various species of the genus *Indigofera* and other plants, such as woad *(Isatis tinctoria),* that contained the blue coloring matter. It was also discovered that a dyestuff with storage and commercial trade value could be obtained by drying the plants or by dehydrating the vat. This derived or precipitated indigo dyestuff was an excellent trade item and usually sold in powder, paste, or cake form.

Kermes, a lac insect found in the Mediterranean area, supplied an ancient red dye, as did roots from the madder plant *(Rubia tinctorum).* Yellow dyes were easily obtained from a variety of plants, and each continent had its favorites. Perhaps the yellow dye made from weld *(Reseda luteola)* was the favorite of early European dyers.

Very early in dye history it was discovered that certain substances could impart color to natural fibers and other natural materials if they were put into a water bath with the fiber. These dyes needed no other substances added to the dyebath. We now call these dyes "substantive" or "direct" dyes. Other dyestuffs do not readily bond to the fiber without an assist from a salt or other chemical; these dyes are known as the "adjective" or "mordant" dyes. There are also dyes which actually seem to physically coat the fiber with color and not bond chemically to it in quite the same way as the substantive or mordant dyes. Indigo vat dye is an example of this physical or mechanical fixing of color to the fiber.

Ancient dyers also discovered the use of metal salts as both coloring agents and as assistants in the bonding of dyes to fibers. These metal salts are called mordants, and some, particularly aluminum and iron, appear to have been in use in Egypt and India long before the Christian era.

With the travels of Marco Polo in the late thirteenth century and those of other explorers and commercial traders, regular trade routes became well established between Europe, Africa, and the Far East. In medieval Europe the dyers progressed to guild workshops, where large quantities of goods could be dyed. The guilds, forerunners of the factories and labor unions, made extensive use of the newly imported dyestuffs and were able to expand their color schemes by adding new dyestuffs to the inventory. They also found they could often combine dyestuffs from the new foreign sources with those from closer to home. Once the explorers reached the shores of the Americas, the exchange of goods and the dye possibilities increased even more.

The discovery and colonization of America led to a new era in European dyeing. Newly found dyestuffs such as the cochineal insects, brazilwood, and annatto became regular trade goods. European dyers had previously developed their color systems dependent primarily on woad or indigo blue, madder or kermes red, and weld or various locally available yellows. With the introduction of the cochineal insect dye—which had been in use in the Americas since long before the Christian era—and the various other American dyestuffs, the dyers could produce an even wider range of colors.

For pigments, the basic color system depends on the primary colors of red, blue, and yellow; all other colors are obtained by mixing the primaries and black or white. By using mordants, the ancient red, yellow, and blue dyes, plus the newly introduced American dyestuffs, the European dyers had a wide range of dye colors available for use on leather and textiles of all kinds.

DYE-HOUSE AT THE GOBELINS, PARIS.

*This engraving from the early nineteenth century depicts a scene in the dyehouse at the Gobelins in Paris, long famous for their tapestries.*

Prior to European colonization of North America, the Native Americans had for centuries been quite skilled at coloring their homes and animals, their tools and textiles, and even their own bodies. The groups of Native Americans differed in customs and religions; their houses, food, tools, animals, and clothing were dependent on natural resources that varied across the continent. Their coloration abilities were both dependent upon and reflective of their environment.

These Native Americans were, as a whole, very conservative of nature. They realized how much a part of the world they were personally, as well as how dependent they were on nature's provisions. In most cases the old proverb "Waste not—want not" was highly applicable. When an animal was killed for food, non-edibles went into leather for houses and clothing, sinew became sewing threads, bones became tools. And in some cases, as with buffalo gallstones, portions became dyes and paints.

Other dyes were produced from plants or earth ochres by traditional putrefaction or heating methods. Paints were made from the same materials. Ground ochres were used to decorate pottery and leather. Juice from plants was used cosmetically and for coloring materials other than the dyer's skin. In Caesar's time the native Britons colored their bodies blue with woad; Native Americans colored themselves with chokecherry juice. An ocean apart, these groups were using the same coloring processes for the same purposes; the resultant color variations were dependent on the resources available in their environment.

When European immigrants began to colonize North America, they brought the post-medieval but pre-industrial technology of seventeenth-century Europe with them. Since European cloth and dye workshops were reluctant to give up the new trade with the colonies, they sent little or no equipment and very few expert weavers, finishers, and dyers to the colonies. This forced the settlers to depend on imported textiles supplemented with home production, which was mostly limited to garments and household linens and blankets. Some very fine colonial

*Dogbane* (Apocynum cannabinum) *bark was used for twine and string by many groups of Native Americans. As a dyestuff, it produces strong colors in the gold and brown ranges.* (Photo: Jan Cornies, courtesy Jones Sheep Farm)

textiles have fortunately been preserved, and of those produced at home, many were dyed with natural dyes made from materials collected by the colonists or purchased via the regular trade routes. Some of the favorite colonial dyestuffs—goldenrod, various woods, indigo, madder, walnut, and butternut—are still frequently used. In some areas attempts were made to grow madder and indigo for commerce, but these attempts were short-lived. There are patches still to be found in the eastern United States of some of these madder and indigo plantings.

The American Revolution caused the colonists to realize how dependent they were on imported goods from Europe, including textiles.

*Osage orange (Maclura pomifera) provided wood for tools and hunting equipment for Native Americans. It also produced dyes for them, as well as the khaki dye for World War I army uniforms.*

*Fingerbraided yarn pouch, thought to be Ojibwa. This finely plaited wool or hair fiber bag is beaded and features a highly unusual resist area in the fringe. The dyed color is a very deep rusty red. Formerly the property of the Earl of Warwick, it is thought to have been collected during the American Revolution.* (Denver Art Museum Purchase)

*Sioux "scalp coat" collected at Fort Laramie, Wyoming, in 1866. Made from two deerskins, it is believed to have been dyed with red and yellow ochers, "buffalo yellow" from buffalo gallstones, and native blue "earth paints."* (Denver Art Museum Purchase)

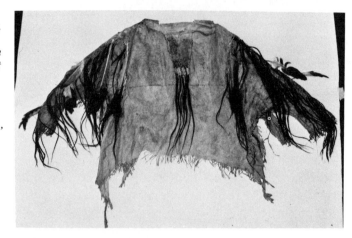

*Chitimacha double-woven checker-weave basket. Made in Louisiana in 1936, the split cane was dyed with black walnut and bloodroot.* (Denver Art Museum Purchase)

Much of this dependency was soon relieved, however, for the Industrial Revolution followed the war very quickly. With it came the establishment of many industries in the new country, including the blossoming of a full-scale textile industry. Spinning, weaving, finishing, and dyeing moved from the guild workshop and the home into the mills and factories. And by the late nineteenth century dye chemists had been able to produce a range of synthetic dyes which almost eliminated the need for dyeing with natural materials.

Although we generally credit William Henry Perkin's 1856 discovery of coal-tar dyes as the beginning of synthetic or synthesized dyes, it is important to remember that coal tar is a natural substance. A truly synthetic dye is one in which a chemical compound is made by combining its elements artificially. A synthetic dye is not a "derived dye," that is, one that is produced by extracting a concentrated dyestuff from a greater quantity or combination of natural materials. Some early dye chemistry was based on derived dyes and from there went into synthesis of the chemical compound necessary to produce a given color.

Several of the commercially important natural dyestuffs were marketed (and still are) in a derived state. When you purchase natural indigo, for example, you will rarely get the indigo in plant form. Instead you will be sold lump, cake, powder, or paste indigo, derived directly from the plant or precipitated in the vat. The plant has undergone one or more of a number of processes, including being dried and pulverized, or being fermented, evaporated, and formed, or it has been made into a vat dye and dehydrated. The results and the product you are being sold are still natural indigo. Synthetic indigo used by the dye industry has the same chemical makeup—that is, it is essentially the same chemical compound as natural indigo. But there is no plant base; instead there are carbon, hydrogen, oxygen, and nitrogen atoms formulated to match the indican molecules of natural indigo.

If it were not for isolated groups or interested individuals who have held on to traditional means of dyeing with natural materials, there might not be any natural dye technology in North America today. The Tyrian purple dye methods disappeared around the twelfth century and are now lost. Some pre-Columbian textiles appear to have been dyed with an iron mordant, but because they have deteriorated, and the techniques of dyeing were not passed down through the generations, we are unable to know just how the dyeing was done. What we do have, however, are textile fragments from antiquity and some early writings (Chinese manuscripts, Pliny, Aristotle) that demonstrate that dyeing with natural materials was an ancient art and craft practiced in many parts of the world thousands of years before the Christian era. But a number of the early technological methods have been lost forever.

*This yarrow* (Achillea lanulosa) *and related species have been used medicinally and for dye by native and immigrant Americans.* (Photo: Jan Cornies, courtesy Jones Sheep Farm)

Fortunately there are today Native Americans who have maintained their heritage and the continuity of dyeing with natural materials while contributing to contemporary life. Many groups are still dyeing yarn and fabric, leather, basketry materials, wooden articles, and themselves while using the same rituals, dyestuffs, and methods traditionally used by their ancestors (frequently for religious purposes). Likewise, pockets of European settlers, isolated from the main currents of American life, have maintained their dye practices and home remedies. They both need and genuinely appreciate nature's healing powers and ability to share colorful dyes. And there are those people who out of interest in the traditional methods of producing dyes from natural materials have done research and taught themselves or learned to dye from an experienced dyer. Thus the traditional ways of collecting materials, processing them, and producing dye are still often practiced in North America.

*This wool-and-cotton coverlet was woven by J. Gamble in 1834 from indigo-dyed wool on a white cotton warp.* (Denver Art Museum Purchase)

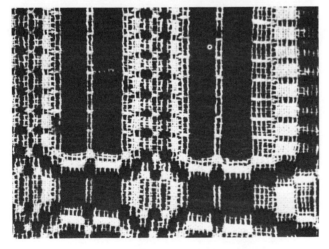

*Detail of a "9 Stars with Divided Table" coverlet woven with tomato-red (probably madder) and handspun wools on a white cotton warp.* (Collection of the author. Photo: Carol Strickler)

*Detail of a "Pine Bloom" pattern coverlet woven with indigo-dyed handspun wool on a white cotton warp.* (Collection of the author. Photo: Carol Strickler)

*"Sunburst" quilt of naturally dyed silks and cottons made in the United States and dated 1849. It is 94" square.* (Denver Art Museum Textile Collection)

*Single tulip detail of a cotton quilt made in the eastern United States around 1825. Note the calico printed designs on the leaves and stem as well as on the lower portions of the blossom.* (Denver Art Museum, Gift of Mrs. Edna D. Greenamyre)

# Chapter 2.
# Types of Dyes and Dye Processes

Basically there are three types of natural dyes that color unspun fibers, yarns, fabrics, leather, wood, and other non-synthetic materials. First are the substantive dyes. These dyes molecularly bond directly with the fiber during absorption into and adsorption onto the surface of the fiber. You might think of absorption of the dye into the fiber as being somewhat like a sponge soaking up water; the whole sponge gets wet, and the water fills up all the holes in the sponge. Adsorption works more like painting the outside of the sponge; the color adheres to the surface of the sponge but is not absorbed internally. Dyes are absorbed and adsorbed at the molecular level by the fiber or other material during the dye process.

Second is the adjective or mordant group of dyes. This group of dyes, which includes a majority of the natural dyes, requires the presence of a fixative to chemically bond the dye pigments to the fibers. Dyers have discovered that the presence of metal salts either in the dye liquor or applied previously to the fiber facilitates bonding of the dye and the fiber at the molecular level. The pigment obtained from the natural dyestuff combines chemically with the metal-salt mordant to form an insoluble coloring compound—called a lake—on and in the fiber. In old dye manuals these compounds were often called by names like crimson lake or green lake or yellow lake, denoting either the color itself or the source of the color. Some of the metal salts affect the resultant dye color as well as the "hand" or feel of the fibers and their subsequent deterioration or discoloration from exposure to light and moisture.

The third group of dyes may or may not require a mordant, and they do not bond to the fiber on quite the same basis as the first two groups of dyes. Rather, these dyes, which include traditional vat dyes as well as some hot water dyes, mechanically attach to the fiber, with the effect of coating the fiber with color. While many of these dyes, such as indigo, may be quite fast to light and washing, others "crock" or fall off the fiber through continued rubbing or washing.

Methods of using natural dyes are as varied as the dyers who actually do the work. There are several basic methods with which most dyers are familiar; however, contemporary dyers, like their counterparts through the ages, use the materials and fibers available to them. And, like most folk artisans, dyers add their own personal touches to the dyeing process. Use of color, particularly color derived from the world around us, is a personal choice, although results of a natural dyebath may often surprise even the most experienced dyer. Except for earth ochres or other minerals, natural dye materials are living things, and soil, water, air, humidity, and elevation all play a role in determining dye color and quality.

Whether the dyer chooses to use an imported, "exotic" trade dyestuff or a "native" locally available material, there are several basic methods which can be used with the dyestuff to obtain the dye liquor.

# Putrefaction/Fermentation

Perhaps the most ancient dye process is that of putrefaction or fermentation. Vat dyes are based on this dye method, which involves placing the dyestuff in a suitable container, adding liquid (usually water), and then leaving the container alone for a period of time. The principle involved in this method is simply that the color leaches out of the plant into the water to form a water-soluble, usually acidic dye liquor which will in turn bond color to fiber immersed into the pot of dye.

There are numerous variations on this putrefaction process. In some instances the container of plant and liquid is put in the sun to warm, thus using solar energy to create a heated dyebath. Many early Native American groups, as well as contemporary dyers, use urine instead of water for the liquid in the container. In some cases the plant is juicy enough, as with prickly pear cactus fruit, for the dyer to simply mash the plant and layer it with the fiber or other material to be dyed in a container without added liquid.

Some other variations include use of a pot made of a reactive metal such as iron or copper to hold the fermenting mass, or the addition of a mordant to it. Some groups have fermented their dyestuff in pots of iron-rich clay or in tubs made of woods rich in tannin; these all affect the color yield. Still other methods involve adding sugar, yeast, bran, or other materials to encourage the putrefaction/fermentation process.

# Water-Bath Dyes

There are some dyestuffs, including both direct and mordant dyes, that work well only in a water bath. These water baths are usually heated, but some of the dyes work in cool water on pre-mordanted fibers; these are close to the putrefaction dyes. Some dyestuffs produce one color at a low temperature like 125° F, another color at a simmer of 175–190° F, and still another at the boiling point (212° F or so, depending on elevation).

The depth or intensity of color obtained from many of these water-bath dyes also varies depending on the amount of time the dyestuff remains in the dye liquor. Some water-bath dyes work best if the fiber, dyestuff, and mordant brew together in the pot at the same time. Other dyes work better if the fiber is pre-mordanted and placed in a dye liquor from which the dye materials have been removed; the liquor is prepared by cooking the dyestuff in a water bath, and the fiber is then cooked in the dyebath. Many dyestuffs, particularly the orchil or purple-producing lichens, must be put in an ammonia or alkaline solution before they will release the orchil (purple) color; other plants need an acidic environment for best color release.

The matter of alkalinity or acidity of the dyebath may be important. It can easily be controlled by the dyer through addition of simple acids (vinegar, oxalic acid) or alkalis (household ammonia, preferably the non-sudsy type). Many dyed colors will vary according to the pH (the relative level of acidity or alkalinity) of the dyebath.

A basic understanding of pH—the relative level of hydrogen ions (H+) in a solution, as expressed on a numerical index—will enable you to experiment with color alteration. The pH scale goes from 0 to 14, with 7 as neutral; 0–6 is acidic and 8–14 is basic or alkaline. As you move down the scale from 7 to 6, the solution goes from the neutral point (7), usually considered to be pure water, to slightly acidic. Each number on the pH scale represents a degree of change ten times that of the next pH numerical rating. So, as you move down the scale from a pH of 6 to a pH of 5, you will note that the pH 5 is ten times as acidic as pH 6 and one hundred times as acidic as pH 7; pH 4 is ten times as acidic as pH 5, one hundred times as acidic as pH 6, and one thousand times as acidic as pH 7. Thus, the lower the pH number, the more acidic the solution.

**pH Scale**

| 1 | 4 | 7 | 11 | 14 |
|---|---|---|---|---|
| Very acid | Moderately acid | Neutral | Moderately alkaline | Very alkaline |

Moving up from pH 7 on the scale, the solution becomes increasingly alkaline, with pH 8 ten times as alkaline as pH 7, pH 9 ten times as alkaline as pH 8 and one hundred times as alkaline as pH 7, and so on. The higher the number is above 7, the more alkaline the solution is.

Not only can pH affect color yield, but it is important to the health of the dyed fiber as well. Protein fibers (wool, silk) generally prefer acidic dyebaths, while many cellulosic fibers (cotton, hemp, flax) dye better in somewhat alkaline conditions. The fibers not only bond better with the dye in the proper pH-level bath, but they will last much longer. For example, a strong alkali bath weakens and will cause rapid deterioration of wool fibers and thus of the yarn or textile made from it. Cotton, on the other hand, becomes a much stronger fiber if it is mercerized —put through an alkaline (lye) solution and then neutralized. An inexpensive roll of pH paper from your local chemical supplier or druggist will not only provide interesting studies and comparisons, but may help prevent bad dyeing and fiber deterioration as well.

It would seem there are so many ways to use dyes that the novice dyer could easily be confused. In actuality, most natural dye methods are simply variations on a theme. Once a few basic techniques have been mastered, you will discover many possibilities for exploration of processes and for the development of your individual approach to dyeing with natural materials.

## Chapter 3.

# Tools of the Trade: Equipment, Mordants, Dyestuffs, and Fibers

## Equipment

Outfitting for dyeing is in many ways similar to assembling utensils for cooking. Since the majority of contemporary natural dyes are hot water bath dyes, the dyer actually becomes involved in a cooking or stewing process—except that the dyer is cooking for color and not for dinner.

*Selected equipment with dried sagebrush: enamel pots with lids, scales, measuring spoons and cups, stir stick, rubber gloves, containers for mordants and dyestuff, strainer, and label tags.*

It is not necessary to spend a lot of money for equipment, even though it is entirely possible to do so—depending on your choice of utensils. Cheaper equipment is not necessarily worse, and expensive

17

items are not necessarily better, either. Basically this is the equipment you will need:

## Dyepots

Consider the optimum weight ratio of wool to mordant or dye liquor to be about 1:30, and that the dye liquor will weigh about 8 pounds per gallon. This means you will need at least a 4-gallon pot to handle 1 pound of wool; a 5-gallon pot will provide even more space for the materials.

The pots should have handles and lids, and they should be made of enamel-covered metal or a non-reactive, non-corrosive metal, such as stainless steel. Other metal pots (copper, iron, aluminum) can be used, but the possibility of free metallic compounds entering the dyebath from the pot should be considered; these compounds can affect your dye color unpredictably. Glass vessels can also be used, but they are more likely to break. Even though the pots may be scoured after use, they should be reserved for dyeing only: metal-salt mordants are poisonous, and most dyestuffs are not edible. Yard sales, second-hand stores, hardware stores, and restaurant suppliers are all sources for pots. If enamel pots become chipped, you may get metal compounds in your dyebath. An easy touch-up with enamel kitchen-appliance paint will solve the problem.

## Heat and Ventilation Sources

Most natural dyers work at home in their kitchens, where the family cookstove provides the source of heat. To avoid possible contamination,

*Dyeing outdoors insures good ventilation and easy cleanup. A hot plate or a camp stove provides the heat. Note the loosely tied string ties on the skeins of yarn, which belong to Mary Lou Wilcox.*

it is best not to cook food and mordant or dye at the same time. A good ventilation system is a must. A vented hood or wall fan, plenty of open windows and doors, and keeping lids on the heating pots will help prevent any toxic fumes from filling the airspace.

An ideal setup for dyeing would include a separate work area with gas heaters for best control of temperature, a good ventilation system, and a source of water with a deep sink for rinsing. You can, however, take advantage of the outdoor areas available to you and heat your pots on a camp stove or a wood fire.

## Water: Washing, Rinsing, and Disposal Areas

Water is necessary for mordanting, dyebaths, and washing and rinsing the fibers. It is a good idea to check your water source for mineral deposits that may affect your dye color. For example, iron can cause a general darkening or "saddening" (graying) of the colors. You can also check your water for pH; rainwater is usually very close to the neutral reading of pH 7, but domestic water in cities and water from wells can vary quite a bit from the neutral point.

For washing and rinsing your fiber you will need either a large tub or a sink. How you are able to dispose of the waste water or extra mordant or dye liquor may determine your selection of rinsing vessel. People who dispose into city sewer systems will usually have no difficulties just pouring leftover mordant and dyebaths or wash or rinse water down the sink and into the sewer system. If you have a septic system, you will be wise to dump the waste onto the ground in an area where you are not growing food crops or where pets might dig or chew growth. Mordants particularly can upset the bacteria level in septic tanks and may cause malfunctioning of the septic system. Mordant baths do contain some metallic elements which help plants (as does iron), but some (like copper) may harm plants if given in large doses. These are natural minerals, and they came out of the earth in the first place; but an excess of any of them can cause problems. Dumping any mordant baths you are not sure about on a vacant gravel driveway may be your best choice. In any case, remember that these natural wastes are preferable to most synthetic ones.

## Miscellaneous Tools and Supplies

You will need some way to stir the dyebath and lift the fibers. Wooden dowels or sticks work well; they should be sturdy enough to lift at least a pound of wet yarn and long enough to reach the bottom of the pot with plenty of hand space to spare. Some dyers prefer to use glass, plastic, or stainless steel rods; others use a variety of implements like chopsticks, stainless steel forks and spoons, slotted spoons, or strainers made of stainless steel or plastic.

A large plastic or stainless steel colander or strainer will be extremely useful for straining out the dyestuff and draining fibers before rinsing and drying.

Cheesecloth or nylon net bags or big flat pieces are useful for tying loose dyestuff; they also make straining the bath after brewing a bit easier.

Rubber gloves are a must to protect your skin from toxic materials and stains. Some dyers also wear an apron, and most wear old, comfortable clothes; one does not wear party clothes while attending a dyepot.

Extra pots and plastic tubs are quite useful for rinsing, dividing dye liquor, and carrying wet fiber.

Scales which accurately measure in ounces or grams will be very useful and are absolutely necessary should you wish to duplicate dyes. Mordant measuring can be done with teaspoons, but a gram scale will provide a much more accurate measurement from which you can determine weight ratios. You might want to shop for a scale which can measure from very small amounts up to a pound or two—or whatever amount of fiber can be accommodated in your pots.

Teaspoons, measuring cups, and other calibrated measuring devices will come in handy; some dyers like to use chemistry beakers. Again, stainless steel, plastic, and glass are the best materials.

A thermometer is necessary for determining the temperature of the baths and helping to maintain a consistent level of heat during experimentation or regular dyeing. Either a glass cheese-maker's thermometer that floats in the bath or a glass candy thermometer that attaches to the side of the pot will work.

Tags for marking fiber or yarn in the bath can be cut from plastic

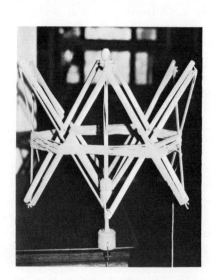

*Use of an umbrella swift will speed the skein-making process as well as provide an accurate measurement of yardage.*

bottles. Paper-and-string tags are useful for marking dyed yarns. Masking tape and indelible pens or lead pencils are also helpful.

A yarn winder, niddy-noddy, or umbrella swift to help wind skeins of yarn will enable you to make skeins faster and more easily than making a hand-to-elbow skein or wrapping yarn around a chair. Yarn winders and niddy-noddies also measure the yardage of the skeins.

Large clear glass jars with lids are good for putrefaction and solar dyeing. Smaller dark glass, plastic, or steel containers are best for storing mordants. If there are small children or unsuspecting adults around, you will need a safe place to store your mordants; a locking suitcase is one possibility.

Scissors, knives, pruners, or other cutters are needed for gathering and chopping dyestuff.

Cardboard boxes or paper bags are good for storing most dry dyestuffs, but cochineal insects (dried) and powdered indigo will do best in an airtight container stored in the dark.

Rags, a good sponge, or paper towels to wipe up spills and a nonscratching scouring pad with scouring powder to clean the pots will be helpful.

Some dyers suggest adding things like clothespins for your nose (for those especially odoriferous dyebaths) and a strong back to the list. An appreciation of the process and a good sense of humor will also be helpful.

# Mordants

While not all natural dyes require the use of mordants, the majority of dyes will benefit from their use; they can provide fastness to light and washing as well as brilliance of color. Mordants are water-soluble salts of metals which help bond fiber and pigment at the molecular level. Without getting into detailed chemistry, one might think of the salt as a sort of electric vibrator in the dyebath, shaking the molecules of fiber and dye until the atomic particles eventually dance around enough to realign themselves in such a way that they are stuck in new configurations. They bond molecularly and cannot shake loose from one another.

Metal salts are among the most poisonous substances to the human body known, although traces of metals are components of our body chemistry. But with careful, safe procedures and storage, even the most inexperienced dyer should have no problems.

General precautions include storing chemicals in a safe place; it is a good idea to keep them away from light, tightly capped in glass, plastic, or steel containers, and clearly labeled. Whether you purchase the metal salts from a chemical supplier or from another source, it is

21

helpful to know their grade: technical grade may contain a few impurities; reagent grade must contain no impurities. The technical grade is usually suitable and much less expensive than the reagent grade. Unless you note a dulling of color or other strange effects from possible impurities, it is not worth the extra expense to purchase reagent grade. It may also be possible to buy the mordants as lumps or crystals rather than as powder. Since fine powders easily become airborne and might be inhaled, lumps or crystals can be safer to work with.

Wear rubber gloves any time you have to handle dry mordants, or mordant baths, or unrinsed wet-mordanted fibers. Some mordants are skin irritants. Have good ventilation going, and keep lids on pots while mordanting; fumes from chrome, copper, and tin are particularly toxic. And be sure to keep children or unknowing onlookers away from mordants. Remember, too, that *you* are a natural material and can absorb mordants and dyes.

The mordants most commonly used are listed below (#1–5); #6 is used with indigo to reduce the oxygen in the bath, and #7–17 are used to alter the pH level or otherwise assist the dyeing. Specific amounts used are given with the recipes in later chapters, and while these amounts are not necessarily consistent from one dyer to another, you will note that they are fairly close. After you have experimented with mordants, you will be able to make your own judgments as to the amounts you will want to use.

## 1. Alum (Potassium Aluminum Sulfate—$KAl(SO_4)_2 \cdot 12H_2O$)

Alum is sold as a white powder or crystal sometimes called potash; it may cause a slight yellowing of the base dye color. Ammonium alum $(AlNH_4(SO_4)_2 \cdot 12H_2O)$ is sold as an astringent and is available at most drugstores. Although it may sometimes yellow the color even more than potassium alum does, and will not provide as high a degree of fastness, it is the least toxic of the mordants listed and is suitable for use by children.

## 2. Chrome (Potassium Dichromate or Potassium Bichromate—$K_2Cr_2O_7$)

Chrome has a reputation for being light sensitive and turning fibers green with oxidation and heat. This process is possible, and it has been used extensively in the dye industry to produce a color known as chrome green. Chrome comes as orange crystals which are extremely poisonous. When dissolved in water chrome looks like orange drink, but it takes only 5 grams to kill an adult. Chrome fumes are irritating to mucous membranes; dissolved or undissolved chrome is a skin irritant.

Be sure to keep the lid on the pot of chrome mordant, use the best ventilation possible, and wear rubber gloves when handling the bath or the unrinsed mordanted fiber. Children should not use this mordant.

## 3. Copper or Blue Vitriol (Copper Sulfate—$CuSO_4$)

Plumbers use large quantities of this turquoise-colored lump or crystal mordant to kill tree roots clogging sewer lines. Copper sulfate is deadly poisonous, very pretty, and can often be purchased at hardware or plumbing stores. Unlined copper pots or boilers can be used for mordanting the fibers in lieu of copper sulfate, but the amount of copper released into the bath is difficult to measure. Copper usually has a greening effect on the mordanting yarn and on the dye results.

## 4. Iron or Copperas (Ferrous Sulfate—$FeSO_4$)

This is the same chemical that is used in minute amounts in prenatal and iron vitamin supplements. Remember that only a few of those vitamins ingested at one time can kill a child, yet many adults take one a day. This tannish crystal mordant is toxic in the amounts normally used for mordanting. You can substitute an old iron pot, rusty nails or horseshoes, or other old oxidized (rusty) iron, but you won't be able to measure the amount of iron freed into the bath. Iron "saddens" or gives a gray or brown cast to the dye results. Old dye colors referred to as drab or buff often depended on iron or iron and tannic acid to impart a tan color to textiles, like "iron buff" cotton of the eighteenth and nineteenth centuries. Iron-mordanted goods may continue to darken or get browner with age. Iron has caused more rapid fiber deterioration than many other mordants. This can be observed on pre-Columbian Inca textiles, where the sections believed to have been dyed using iron have disintegrated leaving areas woven in non–iron-affected yarns. Iron is often used in combination with alum, chrome, or copper to alter the color results, or as a separate afterbath sometimes referred to as a post-mordant bath.

## 5. Tin (Stannous Chloride—$SnCl_2$)

Stannous chloride is an extremely poisonous whitish crystal. Always be sure to add tin to water; never put the tin in the pot and pour in the water. Very toxic fumes will fizz right at you if you add water to tin. Tin is most often used to brighten yellows and clarify reds, but it can erase or deaden reds as well. Sometimes tin is used in combination with alum, chrome, or copper for color variation. Tin has been used surreptitiously in silk processing to add weight to the fiber for an increase in market weight. Tin can make wool very harsh to the touch; many dyers follow tin baths with soap washes to help soften this effect.

## 6. Sodium Dithionite or Sodium Hydrosulfite—$Na_2S_2O_4$

This fine white crystalline chemical is used in indigo and woad vats as the oxygen-reducing agent—that is, it takes the free oxygen out of the dye liquor. Sodium hydrosulfite is toxic and has a peculiar ability to ignite if a quantity of it becomes damp; store it in a tightly capped dark glass jar.

## 7. Ammonia (Ammonium Hydroxide—$NH_4OH$)

The clear liquid used for household cleaning is available at hardware and grocery stores in a strength of about 30 percent. Experiments have shown that non-sudsy ammonia usually has more effect on the dye color; the non-sudsy ammonia does not have the detergent additives more prevalent in the sudsy or detergent ammonia sold. Ammonia is used to make the dyebath more basic (alkaline), thus causing alteration of final dye shades. It is also used to cause a release of color from orchil lichens and some other dyestuffs.

## 8. Cream of Tartar (Potassium Bitartrate—$KHC_4H_4O_6$)

Often used in cooking, this white powder can also be used to acidify mordant- and dyebaths. The effect of this is sometimes a brighter yellow or red, and frequently it causes a softening of wool fibers, which may have been harshened during the mordanting process by the heat and salts of metals.

## 9. Glauber's Salt (Sodium Sulfate—$Na_2SO_4$)

This white or colorless salt often assists the molecular juggling going on between mordant-fiber-dye and is felt by many dyers to cause the dye to give a better and brighter color with better fastness. Glauber's salt is called a leveling agent because the salt sometimes helps color bond more evenly to the fiber than it would with only the mordanting metal salts. It may also help to "exhaust" or use up all the color in the dyebath —the additional salt sets more electrostatic energy to work in the bath, thus causing more bonding.

## 10. Lime or Chalk (Calcium Hydroxide—$CaOH_2$)

This powdery white chemical makes the bath more alkaline. It is sometimes used with indigo or woad vats and with some other traditional dyestuffs, such as weld or madder, for clearer and brighter colors.

24

## 11. Lye or Caustic Soda (Sodium Hydroxide—NaOH)

This white, deadly-poisonous powder is used to change the dyebath to a more alkaline state. It is a caustic component of many soaps and is believed to assist in color brightening. Lye is extremely irritating to skin and can cause a terrible burn. It is used in mercerization processes to strengthen cellulose fibers and cause them to more readily accept dye.

## 12. Oxalic Acid—(COOH)$_2$

Oxalic acid is used to brighten many dye colors; it also acidifies the bath. This acid is extremely poisonous and especially irritating to the skin.

## 13. Table Salt (Sodium Chloride—NaCl)

This familiar edible and necessary white crystal can be used like Glauber's salt to give a boost to dye bonding and exhaustion of the dyebath.

## 14. Tannic Acid—$(C_{14}H_{10})_9$

This acid is mildly poisonous and can be a skin irritant. It is a natural product of sumac, of black tea, and of black walnut hulls. It works to bond color to fiber without additional mordants. Used alone, it imparts a brownish color to most natural fibers. Historically it was an important source of drab colors, as well as being used as a mordant.

## 15. Urea—$CO(NH_2)_2$

Sometimes called chamber lye, urea is just dehydrated urine in a whitish crystal or powder form. Its use in dyeing is to cause the dyebath to become more alkaline, although traditionally urine has been used for several purposes: dye liquid, mordant, additive to a bath, or as an afterbath to "fix" color.

## 16. Vinegar or Acetic Acid—$CH_3COOH$

Vinegar contains from 4 to 6 percent acetic acid, and it can be used to acidify dye and mordant baths or as an afterbath or rinse to alter dye color. Acetic acid in a stronger solution can also be used, but handling it is much more dangerous. Clear "white" vinegar is best and can be purchased at grocery stores, but brown cider vinegar will also work.

## 17. Washing Soda (Sodium Carbonate—Na$_2$CO$_3$)

This white powdery crystal is used for scouring or washing fiber prior to mordanting and dyeing. Some dyers also add washing soda to their mordant- or dyebaths to boost color and affect pH; it has an alkaline effect on the bath.

# Dyestuffs

Most dyers who use native and naturalized plants for their dyestuff seem to go by the premise that if the plant itself has color, it will make dye. And that is just about how it works. Dyers using natural materials may purchase or trade some dyestuffs, especially traditional imported materials like madder and indigo, but most tend to use the materials that occur naturally in their locale or that they themselves have planted specifically for dyeing.

*Many noxious weeds like giant ragweed* (Ambrosia trifida) *make excellent dyes. Ensure good ventilation if there are any allergies to plants.* (Photo: Jan Cornies, courtesy Jones Sheep Farm)

Natural dyestuffs may be obtained from animals (like cochineal, shellfish), minerals (colored clay/earth or ochres), or plants (trees, shrubs, herbaceous plants, and lichens). While modern dyers do use materials from the animal and mineral categories, most produce their dyes from plants. The primary concern today, as it has been traditionally, is with the extraction of the optimum color and fastness from each plant as well as the variety of colors which may be obtained from the same plant by using different mordants, additives, and methods. Dyers today use many different methods and a great variety of plants with a common goal of obtaining a good dye and capturing the colors of nature.

Locating natural dyestuffs is as easy as looking around you to see what's growing. The ivy needing pruning, the fading roses on the bush by the back door, and the pile of weeds pulled from the garden are all likely candidates. On a trip to the country, mountains, or seaside you may find a whole new assortment of dyestuffs for your pot.

Some dyers harvest cochineal if they live in an area where these sucking insects feed on prickly pear cacti. Other dyers know of traditional stands of madder, bloodroot, rabbitbrush, or goldenrod in the same way they learned about the edible wild asparagus, the blackberry patch, or the thicket of wild plums. Either they have discovered the dyestuffs/edibles on foraging trips, or someone has shared a secret with them. Both native and immigrant groups of Americans recognized that

*These* Parmelia *lichens were caught growing on a boardwalk in a wet area in Alaska by Judy Wallen. In dry areas lichens grow very slowly and should be spared in favor of abundant and fast-growing herbaceous plants.*

dyestuff is all around us; finding those special colors that become favorites or those that don't fade requires experimentation motivated by need or curiosity.

When foraging for materials remember that some areas, such as national and state parks, are off limits to collecting. Some plants, minerals, and animals are off limits, too; your area forest service can tell you which are threatened, endangered, or rare. Private property also means private dyestuff, but most property owners are happy to share if permission is asked. Roadsides (except in newly planted areas) are good foraging areas, and if you follow the highway-department mower, you won't even have to cut off the plants. Weeds from vacant lots, florist's throwaways, old vegetables from the grocery store, and tree prunings are easily obtained. Whether you live in a rural area or in an apartment in a large city, just look around you and try what you find. A guidebook to the flora of your area will help you identify your dyestuff, and most university botany departments and county extension service offices have someone on the staff who can also assist you in identifying your discoveries.

Plants tend to produce the most intense color for dyes if they are gathered during or just prior to blooming and used right away. You can use any or all parts of a plant (flowers only, all herbaceous parts, only the root, etc.). This is a matter of personal preference and experience;

experimenting will help you determine if a whole plant will give the same results as flowers only, if it is best to use just the leaves, if the bark works better than twigs, and so on.

When you gather plant matter, it will help to cut it directly into a paper bag or box; plastic bags may be all right if you don't have far to travel, but they hold moisture with the plants, and on a warm day you might find putrefaction going on in the bag before you get home. You can dry plants easily for later use by tying them in bunches and hanging them stems-up in an attic or other dry place. Or you can spread them in the shade outdoors, and store them in paper bags or boxes after drying. For future reference, label the dry dyestuff with plant name, fresh weight, and date gathered.

If you select plants which are growing wild, whether they are native or "naturalized" (introduced) species, be conservation minded as you pick or cut them. Remember that if you pick all the plants, there won't be any to propagate. A good rule is to not take more than one-third of what you find, whether it's a single bush or a field of flowers, thus leaving at least two-thirds to propagate. Noxious weeds are so called because they are impossible (or nearly so) to eliminate, and are particularly damaging or aggravating to agriculture. Often these weeds are the toughest, most adaptable plants around. Use them freely, as they often produce superb dyes.

It is important to remember that plants are living things, affected by soil, water, climate, and elevation. Just as you can add ammonia or vinegar to alter the pH of the dyebath, the soil where the plant grows may be acidic or alkaline, and this will affect the plant and the dyebath. Plants growing in wet areas may be larger but not have such concentrated dye capabilities as those in drier locations. Some plants give one color in the spring and another in the fall; this is particularly true of various eucalyptus species. And because of individual plant differences you may notice a slight variation in color or intensity from one dye lot to the next, even though you used the same plant species, gathered in the same area. Synthetic dyes can also vary in color, although they are not dependent on the personality of plants. Dyes made from the same plant species will usually remain in the same color range, however; and various species of the same genus of plants also tend to yield similar colors. For example, the Compositae family of plants (sunflowers, marigolds, dahlias, etc.) all tend to give a basic range of yellows; aspen, willow, poplar, and cottonwood are related trees and give a similar color range. Most dyers are constantly experimenting with different plants and using them in different ways. All you need to get started is a trip outdoors with a bag and a trusty cutting tool.

# Fibers for Natural Dyeing

Because of the chemistry associated with dyes from natural materials, it is necessary to utilize fibers that have dye sites that can bond molecularly with these dyes. Synthetic fibers rarely accept natural dyes; two exceptions are viscose rayon, a fiber developed from a cellulosic base to imitate silk, and nylon, which can be dyed with logwood for a good black. Most other synthetic fibers based on coal or petroleum do not usually accept natural dyes.

The fibers which readily accept color from nature are many and easily obtained. All plant- and animal-based fibers will accept natural dyes, although some do it more successfully than others.

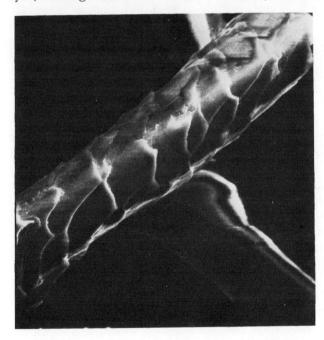

*Photomicrogram showing the scaly surface of wool fiber. During the dye process the scales actually open up to allow dye to penetrate into the internal structure of the fiber. Dyes also bond to the outside of the fiber, at the molecular level.* (Photomicrogram by Howard Abraham, Hewlett-Packard, courtesy of Interweave Press, Inc.)

White wool and silk are generally accepted as the fibers which most readily accept natural dyes. These two fibers can be dyed using nearly the same methods, mordants, and materials, although there are characteristics of the fibers which may require specific handling techniques. Other animal fibers or parts, including hair and skin (leathers), will also accept natural dyes. Light hairs dye easily and well, as do darker hairs and wool. Some interesting coloration can occur from using gray or tan hairs, as they often result in a tweed or "heather" effect when dyed. This is very useful when developing a color scheme, or if you want to get a variety of color effects from a single dyepot. Skins or leathers from almost any animal will accept natural dyes, particularly those based on tannic acid. Barks and woods frequently used for tanning leathers include many species of oak trees, while other woods, like brazilwood, historically played a role in coloring leather.

Native American groups, particularly the Plains Indians, did extensive dyeing and painting of leather. Sometimes an animal-based glue was painted onto the hide and then designs were applied onto the glue with bone tools. These utilized earth ochres, plants, and animal-based dyes (buffalo gallstones were responsible for one favorite color, called "buffalo yellow" by anthropologists). Native Americans also dyed their basketry materials (splints, rushes, twines, grasses) and such articles as bows and arrows, porcupine quills, and decorative wooden items. So-called "primitive" or "uncivilized" groups are worth studying for their technology, particularly with regard to natural dyes, since no synthetic dyes were available prior to the mid-nineteenth century. The survival of these people depended on their ability to understand and work with nature, and they often developed quite sophisticated techniques.

Plant fibers also accept natural dyes, although sometimes not so easily and thoroughly as do animal fibers. "Drab" cottons may have received their name from early dyeings with iron mordants or tannic acid, but many natural dyes simply do not bond as well with plants' cellulose as with animal protein fibers. The result may be drab or buff colors even without the use of iron mordant, since there is often a definite lack in color intensity. Flax (linen), jute, ramie, sisal, wood, and vine products are all examples of plant fibers one may wish to utilize with natural dyes.

With natural dyestuffs and natural fibers, you can realize myriad possibilities for color utilization, brewing experiments, and dye potential. Materials are provided freely by nature or can be nurtured in the home, pasture, garden, or greenhouse. The dyes can be used singly or in combination and with a great variety of mordants, additives, other dyes, and fibers to produce an infinite range of colors.

# Chapter 4.
# Basic Techniques: Scouring, Mercerizing, Mordanting, Dyeing, Testing, and Keeping Records

## Scouring

Before materials can be mordanted or dyed, they must be clean. Any grease, wax, or dirt on the fibers or other materials may resist the mordant and dye, leaving areas which remain the color of the undyed material while the clean portion takes the dye color. Materials which

*Christine LeMar sorts raw wool fleece into bags prior to any washing, mordanting, or dyeing. Her dye garden is in the rear.*

31

have resistant areas can be dyed to obtain mottled or tweedlike results. Freshly shorn or "grease" wool works well for this.

Each fiber has its own peculiarities that will determine the cleaning processes, but no process is very difficult.

## *Wool and Hair Fibers*

Wool and hair should be thoroughly washed or "scoured" to remove dirt, lanolin, grease, and waxes. The scouring process is especially important on "grease fleece," the wool just as it is shorn from the sheep, or on other freshly cut hair fibers. Wool or hair yarns and fabrics which have been mill-processed should also be scoured to remove any spinning oils or other residues from processing. The wool or hair, whether as fleece, yarn, or cloth, can be washed gently with a neutral soap or washing soda in warm water. This should be followed by thorough rinsing. The materials can then be dried outdoors, preferably out of direct sunlight; they can be hung, stretched on a frame, or laid out on an elevated screen (an old window screen lifted with blocks works quite well).

Here's an easy hand-me-down recipe for soap you can make yourself which produces a pH very close to the neutral pH 7:

1. Fill a 3- to 4-gallon pot 1/3 full of water.

2. Add 2 quarts of saved fat (any kind will do, but hard fats from cooking meat are best).

3. Boil the fat and water for 15–20 minutes; then remove from heat to a cool place and skim off the fat. Any food particles will drop down into the water during the boiling.

4. Meanwhile, in a 3- to 4-gallon graniteware or enamel-coated pot, dissolve one can of lye in 1 quart of hot water and let this cool to lukewarm. Do this outdoors and use an old wooden spoon or dowel to stir. Don't breathe the fumes or get the lye solution on you, as lye is very caustic.

5. When the lye has cooled to lukewarm, add the 2 quarts of lukewarm melted fat. Stir with the wooden spoon until it is thick, the consistency of honey.

6. Dissolve 2 tablespoons of borax in 1/2 cup warm water.

7. Add the borax solution and 1 cup of ammonia to the fat–lye solution and stir again for a few minutes. You now have liquid soap.

8. Pour the liquid soap into a glass or enamel pan or a wooden box that has been lined with heavy waxed paper (like freezer wrap). The liquid should be about 2 inches deep.

9. Cover the pan lightly with an old towel or cloth and let the soap sit until it is firm.

10. You must let the soap cure before you use it. (You will know it is cured if you wet a bar and hold it in your hand and it does not "burn" or sting your hand; it should also make suds/lather in warm water—unless the water is especially laden with minerals, i.e., "hard water.") Cut the soap into bars, and store in a box or plastic bag in a dry place for 6 to 8 weeks.

If you are using grease fleece and prefer to scour it with washing soda, here's an easy method to use after sorting the fleece:

1. Shake and tease (pull apart gently) the locks of wool to free it of dirt and loose vegetable matter.

2. Place the wool in warm water (115° F or 46° C) and let it soak for about 10 minutes.

3. Drain with the wool supported in a stainless steel or plastic strainer; do not squeeze, as this may cause matting or felting.

4. For each pound of dirty dry wool, dissolve 1 ounce of washing soda in 2–4 gallons of hot water (125–130° F or 52–54° C—or as hot as your hands can stand).

5. Add and gently immerse the soaked wool, and let it soak in this washing-soda bath about 5 minutes.

6. Drain, supported, and then rinse in clear warm water (115° F or 46° C) with as little agitation as possible.

7. Repeat the washing-soda bath and rinsing as often as necessary.

8. Dry the wool, preferably in the shade outdoors on an elevated screen.

## Silk

Scouring silk is not a difficult process and may not even be necessary unless you have "gummy" silk, which still contains the outer layer of sericin put there by the silk worm as the cocoon is made. The removal of the sericin is called degumming, and most commercial silk yarns and fabrics are degummed before you get them. In case they aren't, here's an easy method of degumming or "boiling off" the sericin. Throughout the entire process remember to change the temperature gradually, since silk has excellent thermoplastic properties which will set wrinkles when the temperature changes rapidly. You can use this to advantage, but it can also be somewhat of a problem if wrinkles set where you don't want them.

1. Weigh the silk and tie the skeins carefully, but not too tightly. Silk is easiest to handle in skeins that weigh about 4 ounces and are tied

in several places with strong cotton thread. Fabrics should be unfolded and handled gently.

2. Soak the silk in warm water (115–120° F or 47° C) for about 30 minutes.

3. Dissolve neutral soap in the amount of about 1–2 cups soap flakes per 4 gallons of water in an enamel or stainless steel container. This is sufficient for 1 pound of silk. The water temperature at this point should be at 115° F or 46° C.

4. Gently remove the soaking silk and squeeze out the excess water.

5. Place the silk in the soap solution and bring it to a high simmer (about 200° F or 93° C). Maintain this temperature 15–30 minutes or until the silk begins to lose its smooth appearance. You can test the silk by feel to find out if the sericin is coming off. If the sericin is off, the silk feels just slightly rough; if the silk feels slimy or slick, the sericin is still present. The soapy bath must be maintained at temperature until the silk no longer feels slick.

6. Allow the silk to cool slightly in the bath—but not too long, as the soap will begin to adhere to the silk as the bath cools.

7. Transfer the silk from the bath into warm water that is as close to the temperature of the cooling soapy bath as possible. Rinse carefully to avoid tangles, especially in fine yarns. Remember the thermoplastic properties of silk; any creases you work into fabric during the washing and later mordanting or dyeing may be difficult to remove. Some sources recommend adding vinegar to the rinse water to neutralize any alkali present in the soap bath; a test with pH paper will tell you whether this is necessary. Should any wrinkles remain in your fabric, it may be possible to press them out by ironing the fabric while wet with a flatiron set for pressing wool.

# Mercerizing

## *Cotton and Other Plant Fibers*

Plant fibers (cellulose fibers) are much more apt to take the dye if they are washed and mercerized prior to mordanting and dyeing. While the animal (protein) fibers easily dye with the acidic dyes nature almost always produces, cellulosic fibers usually dye more successfully if treated to an alkaline bath prior to mordanting. This is perhaps more true of cotton than the other cellulose fibers, but in any case, the fibers must be clean to accept the dye easily and thoroughly. The mercerization process involves putting the fibers through a lye bath which is followed by a vinegar bath to neutralize the alkali. By using care with the lye bath, you can easily mercerize your cellulose fibers and not have

34

to depend on purchasing fibers which have been industrially mercerized. It is easiest to mercerize skeins of yarns or fabrics. Unspun fibers can be mercerized, but the fibers usually shrink to some degree and are difficult to handle without causing matting.

Before mercerization you should scour the plant fibers, a simple process if you follow these steps:

1. Weigh the fiber, yarn, or fabric and then soak it in a graniteware or enamel-coated pot or a plastic tub with hot water (140° F; 60° C) for 30 minutes.

2. For each pound of fiber, yarn, or fabric dissolve 1 ounce of washing soda in 4 gallons of the same temperature (140° F; 60° C) water in a large graniteware or enamel-coated pot.

3. Remove the fiber from the water and squeeze out any excess.

4. Place the soaked fiber in the washing-soda bath and gradually heat to a gentle boil—212° F; 100° C. Keep the fiber, yarn, or fabric in this solution at the same temperature for at least 1 hour, adding extra water as necessary to maintain the quantity.

5. Cool the fiber in the bath, then rinse well in clean water.

6. Dry the material outdoors, in the shade—unless you want the sun's bleaching action to whiten the fiber.

The mercerization process basically involves two baths, one alkaline and the other acidic to neutralize. Here's how to do it. Wear rubber gloves, and work outdoors if possible.

1. Weigh your dry, washed fabric or yarn and place it in a tub of water (about 72° F; 22.2° C) for about 30 minutes.

2. Meanwhile, prepare a frame (a canvas stretcher or an old wooden picture frame without paint will work) on which to wind and stretch the yarn or fabric after the lye bath.

3. In a 4- to 5-gallon graniteware or enamel-coated pot, add 3 ounces of lye to 4 gallons of like temperature water (72° F; 22.2° C); this is sufficient for 1 pound of cellulosic fiber. This is the alkali bath.

4. In a separate 4- to 5-gallon pot mix 3 tablespoons of vinegar to 4 gallons of like temperature water (72° F; 22.2° C). This is the acid bath to neutralize the alkali bath.

5. Drain the yarn or fabric and squeeze the water out. Add clean water to the tub.

6. Carefully, wearing rubber gloves, place the fiber in the lye bath and quickly remove it while squeezing the alkaline bath from the fiber. Try not to splash or drip the bath.

7. Wind or stretch the yarn or fabric on the wooden frame. If you

are using loose fibers, skip this step unless your fiber is in a prepared roving or elongated mass which you can wind gently.

8. Rinse the wound fiber in the tub of clean water. Remove it and replace the water with a new tub full.

9. Now place the (framed) wound fiber, yarn, or fabric in the vinegar bath to neutralize the alkali. Make sure all the fiber gets a thorough soaking.

10. Remove the fiber from the acid bath; keep it on the frame, and rinse it very well in the clean water in the tub. Then, to prevent shrinking, let the fiber dry while still on the frame. Once it is dry, it is ready for mordanting and dyeing.

# Mordanting

The use of mordants may or may not be essential, depending on the dyes you use. For better fastness to light and washing, however, the use of mordants is generally accepted as being a good idea with most natural dyes. Dyers develop their own working methods and ratios of mordant to fiber, as you can see in later chapters. But there are some basic procedures from which most dyers begin.

Mordanting can be done prior to dyeing (called pre-mordanting), during dyeing (the one-pot method), or after dyeing (post-mordanting). In each case the effect of the mordant is to assist the adsorption and absorption of the dye and promote good bonding of dye and fiber. The methods for mordanting outlined below apply to wool, silk, and other protein fibers; cotton and other cellulose fibers usually require use of an additional tannic acid bath, later described. In all cases please keep safe working procedures in mind.

## *Pre-mordanting Wool, Silk, and Other Protein Fibers*

1. Weigh the dry and clean fiber, yarn, or fabric. Yarns should be in skeins or hanks and tied loosely in several places to help keep the threads from tangling. Although tying with yarn of the same type of fiber is acceptable, many dyers prefer to use a sturdy cotton thread or string for tying the skeins.

2. Gently submerge the prepared fiber, yarn, or fabric in warm water (115° F or 46° C) to cover it well. Let soak for a minimum of 10 minutes; 30 minutes or longer is even better. This soaking helps to relax the fibers, making them more receptive to mordanting and dyeing.

3. For each pound of fiber allow 4 gallons of water and the specified amount of mordant. Dissolve the mordant carefully in the water in a non-reactive pot, unless you are purposely using the possibly corrosive metal pots (aluminum, copper, iron, tin).

4. Once the mordant is dissolved, remove the soaking fiber and gently squeeze out the excess water or allow it to drip through a strainer or colander. Submerge the fiber in the mordant bath and put the lid on the pot.

5. Raise the temperature gradually to the simmering point (about 180° F or 82° C), stirring the bath and fiber occasionally.

6. Maintain the simmering temperature for 1 hour, or the period of time recommended. Lift the lid occasionally and stir the bath. Never stick your face right over the bath or inhale the fumes. Keep the lid on when you are not stirring, even for a brief moment. Keep good ventilation going. Do not cook food at the same time you are mordanting.

7. After the hour of simmering, either remove the fiber or allow it to cool in the bath. My own preference is to let the fiber cool overnight and rinse it the next day in cool water, but again, every dyer has an individual method.

8. Remove the fiber and rinse it very well, until no mordant can be seen bleeding into the rinse water. This usually takes at least three rinses. The water should be the same temperature as the mordant bath is when you remove the fiber.

9. When no more mordant bleeds into the rinse water, the yarn is ready to be dyed. At this point you can dry the fiber (away from sunlight) or gently squeeze out the excess moisture and store the fiber in the refrigerator if you're not ready to use it.

## One-Pot Mordanting of Wool, Silk, and Other Protein Fibers

Prepare the dyebath (see page 41) with all dyestuff strained out (some dyers leave the dyestuff in). Add the determined amount of mordant to the dyebath and make sure it is thoroughly dissolved. Immerse the soaked fiber and follow the directions for one of the basic dyeing methods described later in this book.

## Post-mordanting Wool, Silk, and Other Protein Fibers

Prepare a mordant bath as for pre-mordanting. Add wetted, previously dyed fiber and proceed as for pre-mordanting. Note that the time the fiber spends in the post-mordant bath need not be as long as in a pre-mordant bath. Post-mordanting is generally used to alter the color of the dye (for example, iron will brown or gray the dye shade; tin often brightens colors; copper can turn a bright yellow to an olive). Very often this color alteration does not necessitate keeping the fiber in the post-mordant bath longer than 15–30 minutes. Watch the color by peeking frequently into the pot, and remove the fiber when it reaches the desired color. Let the fiber cool to lukewarm and rinse well before drying out of direct sunlight.

## Additives

The substances added by dyers to mordant- and dyebaths to heighten or alter color (cream of tartar, salt, vinegar, urea, ammonia, etc.) can be added during any mordanting procedure or to the dyebath itself. Use of these is a matter of personal preference and experimentation. Trying various methods and recipes and doing your own experimentation will help you decide which, if any, of these substances to use and at what point in the dye process. You will also develop a sense of which dyestuffs to combine with which additives and mordants to get the desired results.

## Mordanting Cotton and Other Cellulose Fibers

Mordanting cotton and other cellulose fibers is not a difficult process, but it is a time-consuming one if you follow traditional methods. You can vary the procedures and the timing a bit, but the results may not be very reliable. Outlined below are three methods for mordanting the cellulose fibers. The first method (alum-tannin-alum) is the most dependable and effective, followed by a simple method using just alum. There are two ways of accomplishing the third method, one of which involves a day's fermentation in the dyebath.

### Method #1: Alum-Tannin-Alum

1. Wash your fiber in hot water (140° F; 60° C) with a good soap or washing soda. Rinse thoroughly. Dry and weigh.

2. For each pound of clean, dry material add 4 ounces or 6 tablespoons of alum and 1 ounce or 8 teaspoons of washing soda to 4 gallons of water. Dissolve thoroughly.

3. Add clean and re-wetted material.

4. Bring the bath to a boil (212° F; 100° C). Maintain the temperature for 1 hour.

5. Cool the bath with the cellulose material in it.

6. Remove the cellulose material and rinse very well.

7. Prepare bath #2 by adding 1 ounce of tannic acid—or the liquor made from boiling about 8 ounces sumac leaves—to 4 gallons of water (for 1 pound of material).

8. Enter the wet, rinsed cellulose material. Bring the bath to a boil (212° F; 100° C). Maintain the temperature for 1 hour.

9. Cool the bath with the cellulose material in it.

10. Remove the cellulose material and rinse very well.

11. Prepare bath #3 by repeating step #2.

12. Repeat steps #3–6. (Or: Readmit the wet material and repeat steps #4–6.)

Your cotton or other cellulose material is now ready for the dyepot.

### Method #2: Alum

1. For each pound of clean, dry cellulose material dissolve 4 ounces or 6 tablespoons alum and 1 ounce or 8 teaspoons washing soda in 4 gallons of water. Dissolve thoroughly.

2. Add clean and re-wetted material.

3. Bring the bath to a boil (212° F; 100° C). Maintain the temperature for 1 hour.

4. Cool the bath with the material in it.

5. Remove and rinse the material very well.

Your cotton or other cellulose material is now ready for dyeing.

### Method #3: Hot or Cold Solution

1. Brew your dye and strain out the dyestuff.

2. Now do one of the following; amounts are based on 1 pound of material.

a. Add 4 ounces or 6 tablespoons alum to the dyebath and stir well to dissolve. Add the clean and re-wetted material. Bring the bath to a boil and maintain for 1 hour. Cool the bath with the material in it. Remove and rinse. This is the hot solution.

*or*

b. Add 1 ounce or 8 teaspoons of washing soda to the dyebath as you prepare it. After the dyebath is ready, strain out the dyestuff and cool the bath. Enter the clean and re-wetted material, and let it remain in the bath for at least 24 hours. Remove the material and rinse very well. This is the cold solution.

# Dyeing

## The Dyebath

Making a dyebath is much like stewing vegetables. The process demands watching the time and temperature, measuring amounts of dyestuffs and water, and stirring the bath occasionally. What the dyer is doing is simply cooking the dyestuff in a water bath in order to get the dyestuff to free the coloring matter it holds and transfer it to the water bath. Some dyebaths are very pleasant to have around; others are very odoriferous. It is wise not to brew dyestuffs to which you are allergic, or at least not do it in the house.

*Betty Davenport separates and sorts lichens* (Lobaria pulmonaria *and* Alectoria *spp.) prior to dyeing.*

Once the dyestuff has been gathered, it should be weighed (even if you plan to dry it for future use, weigh it before you do so). Many dyers use a regular ratio of dyestuff to fiber, often 1:1 based on weight of fresh dyestuff to fiber. While this amount is dependent on the dyer's preferences, a 1:1 ratio is a good point of departure for experiments. In some cases, as with expensive exotic dyestuffs like cochineal, it is wise to consult reference sources prior to dyeing, since 1 pound of fiber can be dyed effectively with less than 1 ounce of the dried cochineal.

*Making a skein of yarn using a niddy noddy, a colonial American skeining device. Once the desired amount of yarn is on the niddy noddy, it is tied loosely in several places to keep threads aligned during the mordanting and dyeing.*

A simple hot-water dyeing process would consist of these steps:

1. Decide upon your ratio of dyestuff to fiber or other material to be dyed.

2. Place the correct amount of dyestuff in a large enough stainless steel or enamel-coated pot to accommodate the amount of material to be dyed based on about 4 gallons of water or dyebath per pound of fiber. The dyestuff may be cut or chopped to help it fit into the pot. You can also tie it in a piece of cheesecloth; this will simplify straining out the dye material later. If your amount of dyestuff is too large to fit into the pot at one time, you can prepare the dyebath with whatever will fit in the pot, simmer the bath and strain out that dyestuff, then add the rest of the dyestuff and simmer the bath again before removing the final load of dyestuff.

3. Fill the pot with cool water to at least cover the dyestuff. You may wish to measure the pH level of the water for later comparison.

4. Put a lid on the pot and begin to slowly heat the water to the point of a gentle simmer (147–158° F or 64–70° C). Some dyers then heat their baths to the boiling point, while others maintain it well below the simmering point. This is a matter of personal preference, but you should be aware that exposing fibers to high temperatures for a lengthy period may cause deterioration and discoloration.

5. Maintain the bath at a simmering temperature (175–195° F or 80–90° C) for an hour or so—the length of time again varies according to the dyer. Then allow the bath to cool with the dyestuff still in it. Some dyers remove the dyestuff prior to cooling; others do not cool the bath before adding the material to be dyed.

6. Strain out the dyestuff. An easy way to do this is to pour the bath through a strainer into a second pot.

7. Meanwhile, soak the mordanted fiber at least 10 minutes but preferably 30 minutes in room-temperature water. If you are going to put the fiber into a hot dyebath, soak it in hot water. Use cool water for a cool dyebath. Try not to shift temperatures rapidly, as this shocks the fiber and may cause a variety of problems such as shrinkage, matting, felting, and wrinkling.

8. Remove the soaking fiber and gently squeeze out the excess water.

9. Place the fiber in the dyebath; then put on the lid and slowly heat the bath to the simmering point (or to the temperature you choose).

10. Maintain the bath at this temperature for 1 hour or until the desired color is reached. Removing a bit of fiber and squeezing out the dye liquor will give you an idea of the color and its degree of intensity once it has been rinsed and dried. I usually aim for the maximum

exhaustion (depletion of color) of the bath and let the fiber cool in the bath overnight or longer, but it can be removed at any time you like the color.

11. Remove the fiber and rinse gently (while wearing rubber gloves) until no more color bleeds into the rinse water. Some dyers add soap or washing soda to the rinse water and then rinse again to remove it. The soap or washing soda may affect the color, so always test a small sample before washing a large quantity.

12. Dry the fiber out of direct sunlight, preferably outdoors. Drying in the sunlight may cause colors to fade or otherwise change, and it's a good idea to test a small sample for fastness before drying a large quantity in the sun.

*Christine LeMar's skeins have labels cut from old plastic bottles and lids. They are marked with indelible pens. She ties her skeins with pieces of rayon fabric tape.*

Changing the pH of the bath can be done after removing the dyestuff or during the dyeing by adding ammonia or vinegar to the bath. You can also add either ammonia or vinegar to the rinse water. Some dyers refer to this as an ammonia rinse or a vinegar rinse. Amounts added can be varied, and if you test the pH of the bath before adding vinegar or ammonia, you will be able to determine how much effect adding various quantities of alkali or acid to the bath will have. In any case, remove the material you are dyeing while you stir the vinegar or ammonia into the bath or rinse water.

## Putrefaction and Solar Dyeing

Putrefaction and solar dyeing can be done in much the same way as a heated water-bath dye. The difference is that one might choose clay or glass jars or pots to hold the dyestuff. The jars are set in the sun to heat to leach out the colors rather than on a stove or fire. Use of a solar oven or mirror reflectors will help the solar brew heat more quickly. As with most primitive putrefaction methods, solar dyeing may take a day or a month to achieve good colors. This will depend on the dye-stuff and the quantities used. The gallon-size glass jars often thrown away by restaurants are excellent vessels for solar dyeing; line the lid with waxed paper or plastic to avoid adverse metal contamination.

An unheated putrefaction or fermentation dye might also be of interest to you. Simply gather your dyestuff and place it in a large enough container to hold it covered with water or urine. Cover the container, or leave it open to the air. Place the container in an out of the way location. When you think all the color has leached from your dyestuff into the bath, you can strain out the dyestuff and add the wetted material to be dyed. Then leave the material in the dyebath until the color suits you; remove and rinse the dyed material. Some dyers claim that moldy dyes do an excellent job; others complain that once a dyebath gets moldy it just won't work. Dyers in the Middle Ages often let wood dyes ferment until the surface became "ropey" or resembled an oil slick on wet pavement. The shiny slick on top of the bath could then either be stirred into the bath before dyeing, or removed and used as artist's pigment.

The other method of dyeing which the home dyer will want to attempt is the vat dye. The use of indigo, purple root, and safflower in vat-dye situations is described in the final section (Part Three) of this handbook.

# Testing Methods

In order to know whether the materials you dye will be useful for other than purely immediate esthetic purposes, it is wise to test the dyed articles for fastness to light and washing. You will want to know whether and to what extent the colors fade or wash out. There are ongoing arguments among dyers about whether natural dyes are more beautiful, more colorful, and more or less fast than synthetic dyes. Of course there are arguments on both sides, but nothing wins like success. We must admit that in terms of maintaining their beautiful and subtle or bright colors over a long period of time and being subjected to a variety of wear-and-tear conditions, many ancient natural dyes have held up extremely well. Old Chinese silks, Coptic wool and linen tapestries, South American woolen garments, Indian cottons, medieval European tapestries, and North American leather and basketry materials—all dyed with natural materials—are proof of the viability of natural dyes. It would be interesting to compare synthetic and natural dyes after an equivalent number of centuries, but we will have to wait for that; synthetics are very young in comparison with the ancient natural dyes.

## Lightfastness

With the advent of synthetic dyes came numerous methods for testing how well various dye formulations would hold up under both atmospheric conditions and hard usage with frequent washings. One method

*The weatherometer is an instrument designed to test fastness to light under controlled atmospheric conditions of extremely bright light and measured humidity. The light source is a large and powerful carbon arc lamp.*

for testing colorfastness is done with an instrument called a weatherometer. This machine utilizes a carbon arc lamp and a container of water to simulate atmospheric conditions of extremely bright sunlight and moderate humidity. The lamp fades samples of colored materials mounted on a cylinder that revolves for a controlled period. These conditions can also be varied for value tests, as with actual spraying of water on the material being tested. Since the weatherometer was developed after natural dyes had more or less disappeared from industrial usage, few natural-dyed textiles have been subjected to this standard test of light-fading.

For this book, a sample of each material dyed by each dyer with the representative recipe or method has undergone weatherometer testing. You will note that after each Centroid Color code number there is a number representing the lightfastness, such as L2 or L5; when the test fell between two numbers, the designation might be L2–3 or L4–5. In the testing, samples were exposed at 10-, 20-, 40-, and 80-hour intervals. At the same time, industrial fade test strips for ratings L2, L3, L4, L5, and L6 were exposed. A standard method of comparing the exposed fibers with the test strips at the 80-hour exposure time resulted in the rating given for each dyed sample.

The industrial code ratings can go from L2 to L8, with each number indicating fastness to light that is twice as good as that of the preceding number. Thus, L3 is twice as fast as L2, and L4 is twice as fast as L3 and four times as fast as L2. Most dyes used fall within the range of L2–L6. L2 is the first and worst to fade, and L6 is the last to fade with the most color remaining; in fact, it is difficult to visually perceive any fading in an L6 rating with 80 hours of exposure. Industry considers various fastness ratings as suitable for certain items but not for others. For example, a woman's wool dress may need a minimum L3 or L4 rating, while a man's wool overcoat may require an L5 or L6. The requirements vary with the fiber used, the depth of the color, the use for which the dyed fiber is intended, and the manufacturer's own standards.

It is interesting to note that some dyes fade immediately to a certain degree and then maintain that color. Other dyes fade so gradually there is almost no fading to be perceived from one end of the sample to the other; one only notes fading between the unexposed portion and the 80-hour exposure. Also, with very few exceptions, all the samples tested held on to some color, even those with "less than L2" ratings. The L2 designated clearly visible fading to the degree of the test strip; however, there was still plenty of enjoyable color to be found. And the equivalent of 80 hours of very bright direct arc light (which is equal to 1.5 times sunpower) might never be applied to dyed materials except over a very long period of time. In any case, comparison of the rating for different degrees of darkness on such dyes as indigo—where a longer time in the dye or the repeated exposure to the dye yields darker colors—lets you see that longer time in the bath (or repeated dipping into it) gives better fastness to light. You can also compare the ratings for dyes prepared from the same plant species but in different areas of the continent and note how close they are in many cases, even though the dye methods were vastly different. Finally, orchil lichens and many pale colors have a reputation for fading easily; you will be surprised at some of the actual ratings for several of the purple dyes produced from lichens, as well as those for many of the paler colors.

Since most dyers don't have access to industrial equipment, it is useful to consider alternate testing methods. Perhaps the easiest way to test for lightfastness is to mount labeled samples of the dyed fiber on a heavy piece of paper or cardboard. Cover half of the samples with an additional piece of heavy paper or board. Then, place the mounted samples, half covered, in bright sunlight for a period of time; industry generally exposes in doubled time increments (10, 20, 40, and 80 hours) to match the indicating numbers which are twice as fast as the previous number. You can determine your own "standard" test; a maximum exposure to light of at least 50 hours is a good beginning point, although 80 hours would be a standard time for industry.

It is possible to do a series of timed exposures by moving the top card which is covering a portion of your dyed samples. Thus, one section gets 50 hours, another gets 25, etc. Then, compare the exposed portions to the unexposed to check the amount of fading. If you test some favorite commercially and synthetically dyed fiber along with your naturally dyed sample, you will be able to make some interesting comparisons. There are many more types and formulations for synthetic dyes than for natural dyes; they can be specially formulated for brightness, for reacting to light, heat, or fiber, for washability, for holding up in salt water, and so on, and you may not be able to determine the kind of dye with which you are comparing your naturally dyed samples. But it is á good idea to test your own dyes, for even a brief exposure may tell you whether a certain fiber dyed with your favorite natural dye will hold up well enough to be considered for a knitted sweater or woven casement fabric.

## Washfastness

Testing for washability may also be important, depending on the intended use for your dyed goods. Some dyes bond mechanically to the outside of the fiber rather than adsorbing and absorbing well. These dyes, which I think of as coating the fiber rather than penetrating it, may eventually "crock" or rub or wash off the fiber. This might happen right away—or take a few thousand years. In any case, here's an easy washability test you can try on samples of your dyed fibers, yarns, or fabrics:

1. Fill a jar with a strong solution of a neutral soap and warm water (the temperature you would normally use for washing the fiber). A ratio of about 1/2 cup soap flakes (you can grate your homemade soap) to 1 quart water is a good one to use for this test.

2. Place a sample of your dyed fiber in the jar. Watch to see if the dye comes off and bleeds into the water after 15 minutes.

3. Next, shake the jar to agitate the sample and solution. Observe any bleeding of dye into the solution.

4. Remove the fiber sample, rinse it in clear water, and watch for bleeding at this point. Check the color and the feel or "hand" of the sample; did it get softer? Harsher?

5. Let the sample dry, out of direct sunlight. Then compare the color and hand of the washed sample with an unwashed sample. Did the washing remove any color? How much? Did the soap affect the color by altering it? Sometimes soap, even a neutral one, is more alkaline than

the dyebath; this may alter the final pH of the sample and thus the color. Then check how the washed sample feels. Is it rougher or smoother? Did it lose body and become limp? What happens after you press it with an iron?

These tests may be important if your dyed fiber is intended for a garment or for another use requiring the ability to hold up well under washing. You certainly will not want to use a dye that washes out or that deteriorates your fiber.

The washability factor is important to the dye industry as well as to the home dyer, for there are some synthetic dyes that do not wash well or hold up well in high humidity. You may have had experience with reds and blues, which seem to be the worst, bleeding color into the wash water. And, many garment labels advise "wash separately" or "do not bleach" or "wash in cool water; lay flat to dry." The reasons behind the labels are related to the dye and fiber in the textile, and industry is required to warn the consumer about care of articles. You can easily do the same for your naturally dyed textiles.

## Color Comparisons: The Centroid Color References

Groups associated with color—the producers of paints, dyes, or cosmetics; those who test soils; and those who design interiors and garments, to name a few—are concerned with color references they can use in order to effectively compare and coordinate their colors. If, for example, a paint producer and a wallpaper producer want to manufacture coordinated paint and paper, they need a reference to which they can compare and match their colors of paint and printing. Just saying make it "bright yellow" or "medium blue" may not be precise enough to allow matching.

One such reference available is the Centroid Color System developed by the Inter-Society Color Council (ISCC) and the United States National Bureau of Standards (NBS), in conjunction with color notations from the Munsell Color Company, to assist with color studies of everything from soil and cosmetics to paint and textile dyes. Although many of the colorist groups, such as the American Association of Textile Chemists and Colorists, have their own color reference numbers, they key into the ISCC-NBS Centroid Colors and the Munsell colors. Therefore, if you dye a color and note the code number on the Centroid Color charts, it is possible to cross-reference your color with the dye and color industry throughout the world.

You may not think this is important, but if your idea of yellow obtained from goldenrod and mine are very different, we might be quite disappointed following each other's recipe or method and getting a far different color. By comparing the color of the dyed sample with the Centroid colors, we can obtain a better description of the color. Therefore, each recipe or method in the following chapters is keyed to a Centroid Color code name and number for easy reference. The color charts and an informative reference explaining the history and use of the Centroid Colors are available from the National Bureau of Standards (see Appendix B). The charts contain mounted color chips organized in sequential steps from light to dark, and each chart contains a basic color reference group, such as yellowish green or reddish purple; these in turn can be keyed into the standard color wheel of primary, secondary, and tertiary colors.

## Other Tests

Industry also tests fibers and dyes for a number of other qualities such as abrasion resistance, stretchiness, shape retention, appearance, dry cleaning properties, and general strength and durability. While it has not been within the scope of this handbook to test for these properties, information about these tests is given in the *Technical Manual of the American Association of Textile Chemists and Colorists.* The Wool Bureau, which is the American arm of the International Wool Secretariat, and the National Bureau of Standards are other sources of test information and materials. These organizations' addresses are in Appendix B.

# Keeping Records

Many dyers don't keep records or samples of their dyeing. As a result, they are often unsure about color yield when trying to recall, from one

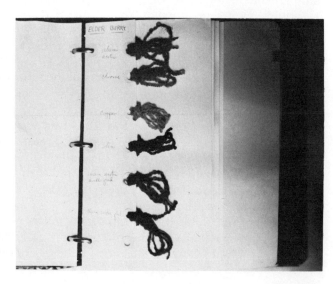

*Margaret Emerson mounts samples of her dyed yarns in a notebook. Mordants used are written next to the sample; other notes are under the folded flap of sturdy paper.*

*Doris Beug mounts samples of her investigative dyeing on sturdy card stock that is cut, folded, and punched to fit a notebook or file box.*

*Martha Omer records gathering forays, impressions, mordants, and dyes in mounted card notebooks. She punches holes to add samples, and she notes locations and warnings about the plants.*

season to another, which source produced which color, and how the dyeing was done to get the color.

An easy solution to this is a simple record-keeping system tailored to the needs of the individual dyer. The system will require some basic information, which can be elaborated upon. Here is a list of some of the things to note about the dye and results; if they are organized to suit

49

*Samples from the author's study of pre-mordanted yarns woven into a sequential fabric, and then dyed. The sample gamps are accompanied by small skeins of dyed yarns.*

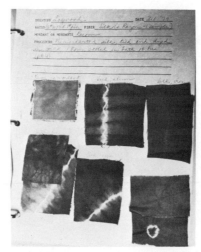

*Sample from the author's study of tied silks dyed using natural dyes. One problem with keeping samples in notebooks is the thickness of the sample. Bulky yarns or fabrics present some difficulties and may be best stored in card files.*

the dyer and accompanied by a sample of the dyed material, the record is kept.

1. Date.
2. Fiber content of the material dyed.

3. Dyestuff (you might want to note where it was gathered, condition of the material, soil, water, etc.).

4. Mordant and additives used.

5. Ratio (note amounts of mordant to fiber and dyestuff to fiber; weight ratios are the easiest to work with).

6. Recipe or method (how you did all the mordanting and dyeing; what peculiarities you noted; what worked and what didn't; etc.).

7. Fastness to light and washing (you might want to include a sample tested for fastness along with comments).

8. Recommendations (note whether it is a good dye, whether it's suitable for the fiber you used, if it's not worth repeating, if you should increase the amount of dyestuff to fiber, etc.).

There may be other interesting things about the dyestuff or dyeing you will want to note. Some dyers record the appearance and odor of the dyebath, particularly if it causes any allergic reactions. Other dyers write poems about the dye or the color. Since these records are personal reference files, you can control the contents and make them as formal or informal as you wish.

The format for keeping your dyeing records is a personal choice. Some dyers keep notebooks; the pages contain the information and holes are punched in the page, through which a sample of the dyed yarn or other material is tied. I keep my records and samples in file folders in a file cabinet. Other dyers knit or weave small samples of dyed yarn and mount these in notebooks or photo albums. This has the added advantage of telling you how the color looks in something besides a single strand of yarn. Some dyers have elaborate cataloging methods. They keep boxes of small skeins, each labeled with a code number to match reference cards kept in a file box. These curatorial reference systems necessitate more storage space; however, they work very efficiently. Other dyers simply label skeins and hang them in a spare closet in an organized color sequence; when they want a certain color, they go to the closet, pull out the skein they want, and attempt to duplicate the dye. Consider your own needs and storage capacities, and then decide on a record-keeping system that suits your interests while maintaining adequate reference information.

# PART TWO

# DYERS:
# THEIR RECIPES
# AND TECHNIQUES

The dyers you will read about in the next pages are only a few of the many artisans in North America practicing one of mankind's most ancient arts and crafts. These are people who are interested in the natural world around them. They have learned from others and through their own experience which materials will produce the colors they seek. Some have very rigid standards and always follow the same procedures. Others like to use a free-hand method, and don't measure quantities of mordants, dyestuff, or fiber, or check temperatures, or watch to see exactly how long the dye brews. Some of these dyers are interested only in experimenting with various fibers, mordants, dyestuffs, and methods; others are involved in production dyeing, using large quantities of materials. Still others attempt consistently to dye a color range from which they create finished articles. But regardless of their attitudes or working procedures, these people are dyers. And they are natural dyers, working with nature's produce—natural dyestuff, natural fibers and materials, water, air, sunlight, and heat. The results of their work are beautiful. Their colors are at once subtle and bold, bright and alive, soft and gentle. There are no color clashes. For these are natural colors —the colors of earth and sky, of a brook on a summer's day, the shades of a desert sunset or an ocean sky at dawn, of newly born spring leaflets or of a fading northeastern autumn. They use nature's paints and dyes —taken briefly from the world outside by people in harmony with nature. These are the dyers who put something of themselves into their colors, and these are their natural dyes.

55

# *Sharon Andersen* | Mexico City, Mexico

Sharon Andersen began dyeing by gathering handfuls of plants, skeins of yarn, an enamel pot, and whatever chemicals she could find. Her pragmatic approach to dyeing is to "try anything once, and if it works, stick with it." Sharon admits to a rebellion of sorts against the synthetic dyed yarn she was able to purchase; she decided to try dyeing with plants as an alternative. A fascination with the dye process and the results gained from working and teaching herself along the way have provided what Sharon terms a "sensual experience." She enjoys everything—from collecting materials through the dye process to the visual delights that result. The vegetable vendor who gives Sharon his rotten prickly pear fruit and wilting marigolds may think she's a *"gringa loca,"* but her dyes prove otherwise.

*1. Dyestuff:* Alfalfa *(Medicago sativa),* cut and dried for tea (which supposedly cures lumbago and is good for the kidneys, says Sharon)

*Fiber:* Wool

*Mordant:* Alum and cream of tartar
(Dissolve 5 1/3 tablespoons alum and 2 2/3 tablespoons cream of tartar in 4 gallons of water per pound of wool. Simmer wool in bath 1 hour; cool overnight in bath; rinse well.)

*Method:* Cover alfalfa with water (1 pound of alfalfa will dye 1 pound of wool); simmer 1 to 2 hours. Strain out plants and add pre-mordanted wool. Simmer 1–2 hours; leave wool in bath overnight. Remove wool, rinse, and dry.

*Color:* Yellow 87, moderate Y
Ammonia added to shift color to Yellow 90, grayish Y

*Lightfastness:* L3–4

*Mordant:* Alum and cream of tartar pre-mordant
Tin (1 teaspoon per pound of wool) afterbath

*Method:* Cover alfalfa with water (1 pound of alfalfa will dye 1 pound of wool); simmer 1–2 hours. Strain out plants and add pre-mordanted wool. Simmer 1–2 hours; leave wool in bath overnight. Remove wool to tin bath; simmer 15–30 minutes. Remove wool; cool to lukewarm; rinse and dry.

*Color:* Yellow 84, strong Y
Ammonia added to shift color produced no change

*Lightfastness:* L3–4

56

*Mordant:* Alum and cream of tartar pre-mordant
Copper (8 teaspoons per pound of wool) afterbath

*Method:* Cover alfalfa with water (1 pound of alfalfa will dye 1 pound of wool); simmer 1–2 hours. Strain out plants and add pre-mordanted wool. Simmer 1–2 hours; leave wool in bath overnight. Remove wool to copper bath; simmer 15–30 minutes. Remove wool; cool to lukewarm; rinse and dry.

*Color:* Olive 106, light Ol
Ammonia added to shift color to Olive Brown 96, dark OlBr

*Lightfastness:* L3–4

*Mordant:* Alum and cream of tartar pre-mordant
Iron (1 teaspoon per pound of wool) afterbath

*Method:* Cover alfalfa with water (1 pound of alfalfa will dye 1 pound of wool); simmer 1–2 hours. Strain out plants and add pre-mordanted wool. Simmer 1–2 hours; leave wool in bath overnight. Remove wool to iron bath; simmer 15–30 minutes. Remove wool; cool to lukewarm; rinse and dry.

*Color:* Olive 110, grayish Ol
Ammonia added to shift color to Olive Brown 96, dark OlBr

*Lightfastness:* L3–4


**2. Dyestuff:** Camomile (*Anthemis* sp.), fresh flowers
*Fiber:* Wool
*Mordant:* Alum and cream of tartar pre-mordant
(Dissolve 5 1/3 tablespoons of alum and 2 2/3 tablespoons of cream of tartar per pound of wool in 4 gallons of water per pound of wool. Simmer 1 hour; cool yarn overnight in bath. Remove and rinse.)

*Method:* Fill a 4-gallon pot with fresh camomile flowers. Cover camomile with water; simmer 1–2 hours. Leave flowers in bath overnight to cool. Strain out flowers and add wool. Simmer 1–2 hours; leave wool in bath overnight to cool. Remove wool, rinse and dry.

*Color:* Yellow 89, pale Y

*Lightfastness:* L5–6

*Mordant:* Alum and cream of tartar pre-mordant
Tin (1 teaspoon per pound) afterbath

*Method:* Fill a 4-gallon pot with fresh camomile flowers. Cover camomile with water; simmer 1 to 2 hours. Leave flowers in bath overnight to cool. Strain out flowers and add wool. Simmer 1–2 hours; leave wool in bath overnight to cool. Remove wool to tin bath; simmer 15–30 minutes. Remove and rinse well.

*Color:* Yellow 82, vivid Y
Ammonia added to shift color to Greenish Yellow 105, grayish gY

*Lightfastness:* L5–6

*Mordant:* Alum and cream of tartar pre-mordant
Copper (8 teaspoons per pound of wool) afterbath

*Method:* Fill a 4-gallon pot with fresh camomile flowers. Cover camomile with water; simmer 1–2 hours. Leave flowers in bath overnight to cool. Strain out flowers and add wool. Simmer 1–2 hours; leave wool in bath overnight to cool. Remove wool to copper bath; simmer 15 to 30 minutes. Remove and rinse well.

*Color:* Yellow 84, strong Y
Ammonia added to shift color to Yellowish Brown 80, grayish yBr

*Lightfastness:* L5–6

*Mordant:* Alum and cream of tartar pre-mordant
Iron (1 teaspoon per pound of wool) afterbath

*Method:* Fill a 4-gallon pot with fresh camomile flowers. Cover camomile with water; simmer 1–2 hours. Leave flowers in bath overnight to cool. Strain out flowers and add wool. Simmer 1–2 hours; leave wool in bath overnight to cool. Remove wool to iron bath; simmer 15–30 minutes. Remove and rinse well.

*Color:* Olive Green 127, grayish OlGr
Ammonia added to shift color to Yellow Green 122, grayish YG

*Lightfastness:* L5–6

*3. Dyestuff:* Cochineal *(Dactylopius coccus);* use 1 ounce per pound of wool.

*Fiber:* Wool

*Mordant:* None

*Method:* Add cochineal to 4 gallons of water. Heat to extract the color (carminic acid when in water). Let bath cool. Add wool to cool bath; leave for 24 hours. Remove and rinse well.

*Color:* Red 16, dark R

*Lightfastness:* L4–5

*Mordant:* Alum and cream of tartar pre-mordant
(Dissolve 5 1/3 tablespoons of alum and 2 2/3 tablespoons of cream of tartar in 4 gallons of water per pound
of wool. Simmer 1 hour; cool yarn overnight in bath.
Remove and rinse.)

*Method:* Add cochineal to 4 gallons of water. Heat to extract the
color. Let bath cool. Add pre-mordanted wool to cool
bath; leave for 24 hours. Remove and rinse well.

*Color:* Purplish Red 256, deep pR
*Lightfastness:* L5–6

*Mordant:* Alum and cream of tartar pre-mordant
Vinegar post-bath (add enough vinegar to water bath to
shift color; add freely)

*Method:* Add cochineal to 4 gallons of water. Heat to extract the
color. Let bath cool. Add pre-mordanted wool to cool
bath; leave for 24 hours. Place wool in vinegar bath
until color shifts. Remove and rinse.

*Color:* Red 13, deep R
*Lightfastness:* L6

*Mordant:* Alum and cream of tartar pre-mordant
Ammonia post-bath (freely add enough ammonia to a
water bath to shift the color)

*Method:* Add cochineal to 4 gallons of water. Heat to extract the
color. Let bath cool. Add pre-mordanted wool to cool
bath; leave for 24 hours. Place wool in ammonia bath
until color shifts. Remove and rinse.

*Color:* Purplish Red 255, strong pR
*Lightfastness:* L5

*4. Dyestuff:* Marigold (*Tagetes* sp.), herbaceous parts
In Mexico the marigolds are favorite flowers to take to
the cemetery on All Souls' Day or the Day of the Dead,
in early November. They are also fed to chickens to
help make their skins golden colored and thus more
appealing at the market. Use an amount of marigolds
equal to the weight of wool.

*Fiber:* Wool

*Mordant:* Alum and cream of tartar pre-mordant
(Dissolve 5 1/3 tablespoons of alum and 2 2/3 tablespoons of cream of tartar in 4 gallons of water per pound
of wool. Simmer 1 hour; cool yarn overnight in bath.
Remove and rinse.)

*Method:* Cover marigolds with water; simmer 1–2 hours. Leave plants in bath overnight to cool. Strain out plants and add wool. Simmer 1–2 hours; leave wool in bath overnight to cool. Remove and rinse well.

*Color:* Yellow 87, moderate Y
Ammonia added to shift color to Yellowish Brown 74, strong yBr

*Lightfastness:* L4–5

*Mordant:* Alum and cream of tartar pre-mordant
Tin (1 teaspoon per pound of wool) afterbath

*Method:* Cover marigolds with water; simmer 1–2 hours. Leave plants in bath overnight to cool. Strain out plants and add wool. Simmer 1 to 2 hours; leave wool in bath overnight to cool. Remove yarn to tin bath; simmer 15 to 30 minutes. Remove and rinse well.

*Color:* Orange Yellow 69, deep OY

*Lightfastness:* L4–5

*Mordant:* Alum and cream of tartar pre-mordant
Copper (8 teaspoons per pound of wool) afterbath

*Method:* Cover marigolds with water; simmer 1–2 hours. Leave plants in bath overnight to cool. Strain out plants and add wool. Simmer 1–2 hours; leave wool in bath overnight to cool. Remove to copper bath; simmer 15–30 minutes. Remove and rinse well.

*Color:* Olive Brown 95, moderate OlBr
Ammonia added to shift color to Yellowish Brown 78, dark yBr

*Lightfastness:* L4–5

*Mordant:* Alum and cream of tartar pre-mordant
Iron (1 teaspoon per pound of wool) afterbath

*Method:* Cover marigolds with water; simmer 1–2 hours. Leave plants in bath overnight to cool. Strain out plants and add wool. Simmer 1–2 hours; leave wool in bath overnight to cool. Remove to iron bath; simmer 15–30 minutes. Remove and rinse well.

*Color:* Olive 107, moderate Ol
Ammonia added to shift color to Yellowish Brown 78, dark yBr

*Lightfastness:* L4–5

*5. Dyestuff:* Prickly pear fruit (*Opuntia* sp.)
This cactus family is a large and prolific one and is the host plant for the sucking insect known as cochineal, which produces reddish dyes. Use enough of the mashed ripe fruit to cover the yarn.

      *Fiber:* Wool and acrylic blend (resulting in a "heather" yarn)
  *Mordant:* None
   *Method:* Mash the fruit in a non-reactive pot. Immerse the yarn
            in the fruit mash. Ferment for 10 days; occasionally
            inspect and stir the bath. Remove and rinse well when
            yarn reaches the desired color.
      *Color:* Purplish Pink 249, light pPk
*Lightfastness:* Less than L2

# *Doris Beug* | South Dakota

For Doris Beug, the dye process is "tedious, time-consuming, surprising, soggy, and infinitely rewarding." She is so involved in dyeing with natural materials that her home now holds suitcases and trunks full of dyed samples and articles made from her handspun as well as commercially spun wool yarns. Doris has borrowed a basic dye-test method from Florida dyer Fred Gerber (he calls it the investigative method) and adapted it to suit her needs. Once Doris has discovered the potential color range using this method, she can dye in larger quantities for such projects as hand-knitted and crocheted afghans, pillows, garments, and wall hangings. Here's how Doris proceeds to test the dye potential for one plant with one pound of wool yarn.

    The wool yarn must be washed and rinsed; it is then mordanted. For the full series one needs 8 one-ounce skeins mordanted with alum, and 8 with chrome. To mordant, Doris prepares an alum bath using 4 ounces alum and 1 ounce cream of tartar for each pound of wool in 4 gallons water. The mordant is dissolved and the yarn is wetted and immersed in the bath. The bath is then brought to a high simmer and the temperature is maintained for 1 hour. The wool cools in the bath overnight; it is then removed and rinsed. For a chrome mordant bath, she uses 1/2 ounce chrome in 4 gallons of water for each pound of wool and proceeds as for alum.

    The dye bath is prepared by simmering the dyestuff (using equal-weight quantities for testing) for 1 hour and cooling in the bath before straining out the dyestuff. The bath is then divided into 2 pots. Eight ounces of alum-mordanted yarn are placed in one pot and 8 ounces of chrome-mordanted yarn are placed in the other pot. The baths are then heated to a simmer and the temperature is maintained for 30–60 minutes. While the dyebaths are simmering, prepare the following mordant solutions for each bath (one for alum and one for chrome): (1) 1/8 teaspoon tin plus 1 teaspoon cream of tartar in 1 cup water; (2) 1/8 ounce copper in 1 cup water; and (3) 1 teaspoon iron in 1 cup water.

Once the dyebaths have simmered the desired length of time, remove all 8 skeins from each bath and set them aside without rinsing. For each set of skeins do the following:

1. Take 1 skein and rinse it until the water is clear. This is skein *a*.

2. Dip a small amount of the dyebath into a pan and add 1 tablespoon clear ammonia. Add a second skein and heat the bath while stirring gently until the color change is completed. Remove it from the bath and rinse well. This is skein *b*.

3. The remaining dyebath is now divided into three small pans. Add one of the mordant solutions to each, and be sure to keep track of them. Two skeins are added to each solution. Simmer gently for 10–15 minutes. Remove the skeins and rinse one of each.

4. Add 1 tablespoon of ammonia to each of the baths, and return the unrinsed skeins to the proper baths. Simmer until the color shifts. Remove and rinse.

The skeins are labeled as follows:

    a. Alum or Chrome
    b. Alum/ammonia or Chrome/ammonia
    c. Alum/tin/tartar or Chrome/tin/tartar
    d. Alum/tin/tartar/ammonia or Chrome/tin/tartar/ammonia
    e. Alum/copper or Chrome/copper
    f. Alum/copper/ammonia or Chrome/copper/ammonia
    g. Alum/iron or Chrome/iron
    h. Alum/iron/ammonia or Chrome/iron/ammonia

Doris usually cuts tags from plastic bottles and uses waterproof markers to write on them just as soon as they are removed from the baths. Using this method, Doris has obtained the following series of colors from plants growing in her area of the northern Great Plains:

    *1. Dyestuff:* Goldenrod (*Solidago* sp.)
      *Mordant:* Alum
        *Color:* Yellow 90, grayish Y
  *Lightfastness:* L4–5
      *Mordant:* Alum/ammonia
        *Color:* Yellow 90, grayish Y
  *Lightfastness:* L4–5
      *Mordant:* Alum/ammonia/tartar
        *Color:* Yellow 82, vivid Y

*Lightfastness:* L5
   *Mordant:* Alum/copper
      *Color:* Yellow 82, vivid Y
*Lightfastness:* L5
   *Mordant:* Alum/copper/ammonia
      *Color:* Olive 109, light grayish Ol
*Lightfastness:* L5–6
   *Mordant:* Alum/iron
      *Color:* Olive 106, light Ol
*Lightfastness:* L5–6
   *Mordant:* Alum/iron/ammonia
      *Color:* Olive 110, grayish Ol
*Lightfastness:* L5–6
   *Mordant:* Chrome
      *Color:* Brown 62, dark grayish Br
*Lightfastness:* L6
   *Mordant:* Chrome/ammonia
      *Color:* Yellowish Brown 76, light yBr
*Lightfastness:* L6
   *Mordant:* Chrome/tin/tartar
      *Color:* Orange Yellow 72, dark OY
*Lightfastness:* L5–6
   *Mordant:* Chrome/tin/tartar/ammonia
      *Color:* Yellow 88, dark Y
*Lightfastness:* L5–6
   *Mordant:* Chrome/copper
      *Color:* Yellow 85, deep Y
*Lightfastness:* L5–6
   *Mordant:* Chrome/copper/ammonia
      *Color:* Olive 106, light Ol
*Lightfastness:* L5–6
   *Mordant:* Chrome/iron
      *Color:* Olive 107, moderate Ol
*Lightfastness:* L5–6
   *Mordant:* Chrome/iron/ammonia
      *Color:* Olive Brown 95, moderate OlBr
*Lightfastness:* L5–6

  *2. Dyestuff:* Tansy *(Tanacetum vulgare)*
            Tansy is a common plant found abundantly in many
            areas of North America.
   *Mordant:* Alum
      *Color:* Yellow 87, moderate Y

*Lightfastness:* L5–6 (the color browned with exposure to light)
  *Mordant:* Alum/ammonia
    *Color:* Yellow 88, dark Y
*Lightfastness:* L5–6 (the color browned with exposure to light)
  *Mordant:* Alum/tin/tartar
    *Color:* Yellow 84, strong Y
*Lightfastness:* L5–6 (the color browned with exposure to light)
  *Mordant:* Alum/tin/tartar/ammonia
    *Color:* Yellow 82, vivid Y
*Lightfastness:* L5–6 (the color browned with exposure to light)
  *Mordant:* Alum/copper
    *Color:* Yellow 91, dark grayish Y
*Lightfastness:* L6
  *Mordant:* Alum/copper/ammonia
    *Color:* Olive Brown 95, moderate OlBr
*Lightfastness:* L6
  *Mordant:* Alum/iron
    *Color:* Olive 110, grayish Ol
*Lightfastness:* L6
  *Mordant:* Alum/iron/ammonia
    *Color:* Olive Brown 96, dark OlBr
*Lightfastness:* L6
  *Mordant:* Chrome
    *Color:* Yellow 85, deep Y
*Lightfastness:* L5–6
  *Mordant:* Chrome/ammonia
    *Color:* Olive Brown 94, light OlBr
*Lightfastness:* L5–6
  *Mordant:* Chrome/tin/tartar
    *Color:* Yellow 91, dark grayish Y
*Lightfastness:* L5–6
  *Mordant:* Chrome/tin/tartar/ammonia
    *Color:* Yellow 88, dark Y
*Lightfastness:* L5–6
  *Mordant:* Chrome/copper
    *Color:* Olive Brown 94, light OlBr
*Lightfastness:* L5–6
  *Mordant:* Chrome/copper/ammonia
    *Color:* Olive Brown 95, moderate OlBr
*Lightfastness:* L5–6
  *Mordant:* Chrome/iron
    *Color:* Olive 110, grayish Ol
*Lightfastness:* L5–6

*Mordant:* Chrome/iron/ammonia
*Color:* Olive Brown 96, dark OlBr
*Lightfastness:* L5–6

**3. Dyestuff:** Maximilian sunflower *(Helianthus maximiliani)*
This perennial sunflower is commonly found in sandy
waste areas of the prairie; it attains a height of 3–4 feet.

*Maximilian sunflower* (Helianthus maximiliani) *is a common midwestern prairie plant which produces an amazingly versatile color range.* (Photo: Jan Cornies, courtesy Jones Sheep Farm)

*Mordant:* Alum
*Color:* Yellow 87, moderate Y
*Lightfastness:* L5
*Mordant:* Alum/ammonia
*Color:* Orange Yellow 69, deep OY
*Lightfastness:* L5–6
*Mordant:* Alum/tin/tartar
*Color:* Yellow 84, strong Y
*Lightfastness:* L5–6
*Mordant:* Alum/tin/tartar/ammonia
*Color:* Yellow 85, deep Y
*Lightfastness:* L5–6
*Mordant:* Alum/copper
*Color:* Olive Brown 95, moderate OlBr
*Lightfastness:* L6
*Mordant:* Alum/copper/ammonia
*Color:* Yellowish Brown 74, strong yBr
*Lightfastness:* L6

65

*Mordant:* Alum/iron
*Color:* Olive 111, dark grayish Ol
*Lightfastness:* L6
*Mordant:* Alum/iron/ammonia
*Color:* Olive Brown 96, dark OlBr
*Lightfastness:* L5–6
*Mordant:* Chrome
*Color:* Orange Yellow 72, dark OY
*Lightfastness:* L5–6
*Mordant:* Chrome/ammonia
*Color:* Reddish Orange 38, dark rO
*Lightfastness:* L4
*Mordant:* Chrome/tin/tartar
*Color:* Yellow 87, moderate Y
*Lightfastness:* L4–5
*Mordant:* Chrome/tin/tartar/ammonia
*Color:* Yellow 84, strong Y
*Lightfastness:* L5
*Mordant:* Chrome/copper
*Color:* Orange 54, brownish orange
*Lightfastness:* L5
*Mordant:* Chrome/copper/ammonia
*Color:* Brown 55, strong Br
*Lightfastness:* L5
*Mordant:* Chrome/iron
*Color:* Brown 56, deep Br
*Lightfastness:* L5
*Mordant:* Chrome/iron/ammonia
*Color:* Brown 56, deep Br
*Lightfastness:* L5

*4. Dyestuff:* Wild plum (*Prunus* sp.), roots
Thickets of these wild fruit trees are found across North America; they particularly favor growing in sub-irrigated soils along rivers and streams.
*Mordant:* Alum
*Color:* Yellowish Pink 28, light yPk
*Lightfastness:* L4–5
*Mordant:* Alum/ammonia
*Color:* Yellowish Pink 29, moderate yPk
*Lightfastness:* L4–5
*Mordant:* Tin (note: no alum used)
*Color:* Yellowish Pink 30, dark yPk

*Lightfastness:* L2–3
    *Mordant:* Tin/ammonia (note: no alum used)
      *Color:* Red 19, grayish R
*Lightfastness:* L2–3
    *Mordant:* Copper (note: no alum used)
      *Color:* Reddish Brown 43, moderate rBr
*Lightfastness:* L5
    *Mordant:* Copper/ammonia (note: no alum used)
      *Color:* Reddish Brown 42, light rBr
*Lightfastness:* L5
    *Mordant:* Iron (note: no alum used)
      *Color:* Red 23, dark reddish gray
*Lightfastness:* L5
    *Mordant:* Iron/ammonia (note: no alum used)
      *Color:* Red 23, dark reddish gray
*Lightfastness:* L5

# *Betty Davenport* | Washington State

Betty Davenport's fascination with lichens began when she was unable to obtain mordants and could find no one to help her pursue dyeing with other materials. Lichen, she found, could simply be put in a pot with water and yarn and simmered until she liked the dyed color.

*Lichens and handspun wool yarns simmering in vinegar-water on Betty Davenport's stove.* (Photo: Betty Davenport)

There are three major types of lichens: (1) foliose or leaf-like, (2) fruticose or shrubby or hair-like, and (3) crustose or crust-like. Li-

67

chens can be found on rocks, tree bark, and soil. As they obtain their moisture and nutrients directly from the air, they are very susceptible to air pollution. Lichens grow very slowly, and they may not be plentiful in all areas. There are, however, some species which are quite abundant; they fall off trees and rocks, and may be picked from dead tree branches.

When gathering lichens, collect only what you need, and never take more than a third of what you find. Collecting lichens that have fallen on the ground before picking those still growing on trees is the best plan for collecting.

Betty takes a supply of plastic bags in her pack on hikes. The lichens are collected by species into the bags, and upon returning home are spread to dry on newspaper for several days. They can then be stored in open plastic bags or other containers that allow for air circulation. Before using the lichens for dye, any bark or twigs must be removed, as they would affect the dyed color.

Betty's record system consists of lichens mounted on file cards with notes on identification, the location where they were collected, the dye method, and any mordants or pH alteratives added. Samples of dyed yarn are then attached to the cards for future reference.

In order to dye with lichens, Betty recommends this simple procedure.

1. Weigh the lichens, crush them, and place them in a non-reactive pot.

2. Cover with water and add a dash of vinegar or ammonia.

3. Add a skein of wool equal in weight to that of the dry lichens.

4. Heat the pot and allow it to simmer until the desired depth of color is obtained. This may take 30 minutes or all day, depending on the lichen.

To obtain the following resultant dyes, skeins of wool were dyed with each lichen using these mordants and alteratives:

1. 1–2 tablespoons vinegar per quart of water in the pot
2. 1–2 tablespoons ammonia per quart of water in the pot
3. 1/8 teaspoon tin added to the vinegar bath
4. 1/8 teaspoon tin added to the ammonia bath

*1. Dyestuff:* Wolf moss *(Letharia vulpina)*
This lichen was important to the trading economy of the Indian groups in the Pacific Northwest. The lichen grows on pine trees on the eastern side of the coastal

mountain ranges and was traded to peoples living along the coast. This plentiful lichen, often used with urine in the dyebath, provided the yellow for many Chilkat blankets.

*Mordant:* Vinegar
*Color:* Yellow 83, brilliant Y
*Lightfastness:* L6
*Mordant:* Vinegar and tin
*Color:* Yellow 83, brilliant Y
*Lightfastness:* L6
*Mordant:* Ammonia and vinegar
*Color:* Yellow 84, strong Y
*Lightfastness:* L6

**2. *Dyestuff:*** Lungwort *(Lobaria pulmonaria)*
Betty gathers this lichen after windstorms that blow the lichens off the trees. It grows on trees on the western side of the Cascade Mountains, and it develops rich colors after simmering about 4 hours. Several skeins can be dyed in successively longer time periods to produce a sequence of colors.

*Mordant:* Ammonia
*Color:* Brown 58, moderate Br
*Lightfastness:* L5–6
*Mordant:* Ammonia and tin
*Color:* Yellowish Brown 75, deep yBr
*Lightfastness:* L5–6
*Mordant:* Vinegar
*Color:* Orange Yellow 72, dark OY
*Lightfastness:* L5–6
*Mordant:* Vinegar and tin
*Color:* Orange Yellow 69, deep OY
*Lightfastness:* L5

**3. *Dyestuff:*** Worm lichen *(Thamnolia subuliformis)*
This whitish ground lichen of alpine zones should be collected sparingly as it grows quite slowly. A small handful will dye several ounces of wool to be used for a very special project.

*Mordant:* Vinegar (1/2-hour simmer)
*Color:* Orange Yellow 68, strong OY
*Lightfastness:* L3–4
*Mordant:* Vinegar (2-hours simmer)

69

*Color:* Orange Yellow 69, deep OY
*Lightfastness:* L6
*Mordant:* Vinegar and tin
*Color:* Orange Yellow 68, strong OY
*Lightfastness:* L6
*Mordant:* Ammonia (2-hours simmer)
*Color:* Yellowish Brown 77, moderate yBr
*Lightfastness:* L2–3

**4. *Dyestuff:*** Orchil lichen (*Umbilicaria* spp.)
To get the orchil or purple color to leach out of the lichen into solution, Betty crushes about 2 tablespoons dry lichen into a glass quart jar, adds 2 tablespoons ammonia, and fills the jar with water. The jar is then left to ferment for 10 days or more, until the liquid becomes a dark purple. Then the yarn is either added to the jar and left to ferment until the desired purple color is obtained, or the liquid in the jar is added to more water in a pot and gently simmered with the yarn to obtain the color. Using the fermentation method, the following colors were obtained with *Umbilicaria* species collected in two locations, one an arid semi-desert, the other a moist mountainous area.

*Species:* Columbia Basin (semi-arid/desert) *Umbilicaria*
*Color:* On handspun wool—Reddish Purple 240, light rP
*Lightfastness:* L2
*Species:* Columbia Basin (semi-arid/desert) *Umbilicaria*
*Color:* On commercially spun wool—Reddish Purple 238, deep rP
*Lightfastness:* L2
*Species:* Cascade Mountain (moist) *Umbilicaria*
*Color:* Reddish Purple 244, pale rP
*Lightfastness:* Less than L2

**5. *Dyestuff:*** Old-man's-beard *(Usnea longissima)*
This very long, gray-green lichen grows on trees in very wet places such as the western side of Washington's Olympic Peninsula; other species of *Usnea* are found in various areas of North America. The simmering bath method produced these results from this stringy, tree-growing lichen.

*Mordant:* Ammonia
*Color:* Yellow 90, grayish Y
*Lightfastness:* L5–6

    *Mordant:* Vinegar
       *Color:* Yellow 89, pale Y
*Lightfastness:* L5–6
    *Mordant:* Vinegar and tin
       *Color:* Yellow 92, yellowish white (very pale)
*Lightfastness:* L5–6

# *Margaret Emerson* | Montana

Enjoying a bit of magic in seeing colors emerge from her dye pots while keeping up with a busy schedule has led Margaret Emerson into the development of an easy method of testing dye potential which she calls consecutive dyeing. The method is a simple one designed to fit into anyone's schedule, and it provides a good range of colors from one dyestuff, one pot, several mordants, and several skeins of wool yarn.

Here is Margaret's "consecutive dyeing" method:

1. Simmer lots of dyestuff in water to cover for at least an hour.
2. Strain out the dyestuff.
3. Add alum mordant (4 tablespoons per pound of wool); stir to dissolve it in the bath.
4. Add skeined wool, either wet or dry, and submerge it completely in the dyebath.
5. Simmer at least 1 hour, adding more water if needed to replace that lost to evaporation. The heat can be turned off and on as one leaves the house, gets busy, etc. The dyeing can go on for several days if necessary.
6. Remove the wool when you like the color, and note the shade of the alum-mordanted wool.
7. Then add chrome (3 teaspoons per pound of wool), or copper (2 tablespoons per pound of wool), or tin (1–2 teaspoons per pound of wool) to the dyebath and dissolve it by stirring thoroughly. Keep in mind that the chrome may brown the color, copper may green it, and tin may turn yellows to orange; decide what color change you want before adding the second mordant.
8. Add all or a portion of the alum-mordanted dyed wool to the bath and proceed as in step 5. If you use a selection of small skeins, you can withhold some and still have some to add for a second color.
9. Remove and rinse.
10. If you have any more dyestuff, you can add it to the bath to strengthen it, as the dyebath may be getting weak. Simmer this at least 1 hour and strain out the dyestuff.

11. Add iron mordant (2 tablespoons per pound of wool) and stir to dissolve.

12. Add all or part of the wool yarn (previously mordanted and dyed in the pot) and repeat steps 5 and 6.

13. Remove and rinse.

The consecutive-dyeing method is easy and flexible. It needs no schedule, since you manage the pots when you want to or have time. And best of all, the method produced these fine colors for Margaret Emerson. She is a dyer who loves plants, the colors they produce, and the fragrance of the dyed yarns.

*1. Dyestuff:* Sagebrush (*Artemesia* spp.)

The western portions of North America have a number of species of *Artemesia* which grow primarily in open, dry areas. *Artemesia* species belong to the Compositae family of plants, to which sunflowers and marigolds also belong.

*Sage* (Artemesia *spp.) is a common plant genus found throughout most of the western half of North America. It produces excellent and bright colors.* (Photo: Jan Cornies, courtesy Jones Sheep Farm)

  *Mordant:* Alum
   *Color:* Greenish Yellow 104, pale gY
*Lightfastness:* L5–6
  *Mordant:* Chrome
   *Color:* Greenish Yellow 105, grayish gY
*Lightfastness:* L5–6
  *Mordant:* Copper
   *Color:* Greenish Yellow 103, dark gY
*Lightfastness:* L5–6
  *Mordant:* Tin

*Color:* Greenish Yellow 97, vivid gY
*Lightfastness:* L5–6
*Mordant:* Tin and ammonia (enough ammonia to shift color)
*Color:* Olive 108, dark Ol
*Lightfastness:* L5–6

**2. Dyestuff:** Black walnut *(Juglans nigra),* green hulls
This dyestuff produces a traditional range of browns and tans; it has been used to stain wood furniture as well as for a variety of dyes.
*Mordant:* None
*Color:* Brown 58, moderate Br
*Lightfastness:* L5–6
*Mordant:* Alum
*Color:* Yellowish Brown 76, light yBr
*Lightfastness:* L5–6
*Mordant:* Chrome
*Color:* Yellowish Brown 77, moderate yBr
*Lightfastness:* L5–6
*Mordant:* Tin and ammonia (add enough to shift color)
*Color:* Reddish Brown 46, grayish rBr
*Lightfastness:* L5–6
*Mordant:* Iron
*Color:* Brown 65, brownish black
*Lightfastness:* L5–6

**3. Dyestuff:** Carrot *(Daucus carota),* tops
This dyestuff is easy to collect when you harvest carrots from the garden. The pleasant smelling bath produces a series of happy colors.
*Mordant:* Alum
*Color:* Greenish Yellow 104, pale gY
*Lightfastness:* L5–6
*Mordant:* Chrome
*Color:* Greenish Yellow 103, dark gY
*Lightfastness:* L5–6
*Mordant:* Chrome and ammonia (add enough ammonia to shift color)
*Color:* Green 149, pale G
*Lightfastness:* L5–6

**4. Dyestuff:** Cascara *(Cascara sagrada),* bark
The aromatic bark of the cascara tree is the basis for many favorite home remedies.

     *Mordant:* Alum, tin, and tartar
        *Color:* Yellow 87, moderate Y
*Lightfastness:* L4–5
     *Mordant:* Alum and chrome
        *Color:* Brown 55, strong Br
*Lightfastness:* L4–5
     *Mordant:* Alum, tin, and tartar, with ammonia rinse
        *Color:* Yellowish Brown 76, light yBr
*Lightfastness:* L4–5
     *Mordant:* Alum, chrome, and ammonia rinse
        *Color:* Brown 55, strong Br
*Lightfastness:* L4–5

# *Virginia Ericson* | Arkansas

Virginia Ericson is one of those individuals fortunate enough to have had a teacher wise in the ways of nature. Her grandmother was the local midwife and folk doctor; she had no education except what experience taught her. This same grandmother taught Virginia which plants made good salves and which made good dyes. She imparted to her young granddaughter the knowledge that nature provides the necessary things of life if one just knows where to look.

Virginia now dyes as her grandmother did long ago—layering dyestuff and unspun wool in a pot, pouring on a dissolved mordant and water mixture, and simmering it on a wood fire until the desired color is reached. Virginia breaks a few rules generally thought to be unbreakable in natural dyeing. She always uses an old aluminum kettle, and she uses the "cup of your hand" to measure mordant "the size of a robin's egg."

Once the desired color is obtained, the kettle is taken off the coals to cool overnight. She then rinses carefully and gently teases out any remnants of dyestuff. The wool is put on a screen to dry, since it was "dyed in the wool," not in the already-spun state.

Then, says Virginia, she likes to "stand back and drink in the beauty," as she feels her grandmother's hand on her shoulder and hears her saying, "It is so simple; there's beauty all around us if we learn how to use God's gifts." As Virginia admits, she just goes on "doing it my way —and grandmother's" and getting lovely, subtle colors in a very natural way.

    *1. Dyestuff:* Queen anne's lace (*Daucus* sp.)
      *Mordant:* Alum

      *Color:* Greenish Yellow 104, pale gY
*Lightfastness:* L3

    **2. *Dyestuff:*** Ragweed (*Ambrosia* sp.)
      *Mordant:* Alum
        *Color:* Greenish Yellow 105, grayish gY
*Lightfastness:* L5

*This common, abundant ragweed* (Ambrosia psilostachya) *is responsible for a lot of hay fever, but it also brews a fine dye.* (Photo: Jan Cornies, courtesy Jones Sheep Farm)

    **3. *Dyestuff:*** Spanish needles *(Bidens bipinnata)*
      *Mordant:* Alum
        *Color:* Orange 52, light O
*Lightfastness:* L4–5

    **4. *Dyestuff:*** Sumac (*Rhus* sp.)
      *Mordant:* None; dyed in aluminum kettle
        *Color:* Gray 266, dark gray
*Lightfastness:* Light: L6

## *Mary Eleanor Forsyth* | Michigan

Living in a rural farming area has provided spinner, weaver, and dyer Mary Forsyth with pleasant days in the fields and woods as well as with a great variety of plants to brew for dye. Mary has access to many trees and shrubs in addition to herbaceous plants, and she experiments freely with them.

    The use of colors from plants is like a diary or a good photograph album, says Mary, and taking out her sassafras-dyed yarn in the dead of winter reminds her of the day she and her brother cut fence posts from sassafras trees and pulled roots for tea and dye. Mary usually dyes her own handspun yarn and notes that after dyeing, the skeins can be hung from a rod or line with a weight attached that is just heavy enough to keep the twist in the yarn even. The resultant yarn will have less tendency to twist back upon itself and kink if weighted when drying.

Using well water from a "superior" well, plants from her area, and her own intuition has provided Mary Forsyth with these colors of summer to be brought out on a winter's day.

*1. Dyestuff:* Birch (*Betula* sp.), small green twigs cut into smaller pieces
   *Ratio:* 1:1 weight ratio in 3 gallons of water in a non-reactive, lidded pot
*Mordant:* 2 ounces of alum dissolved in 2 gallons of water for 4 ounces of wool
   (Simmer 1 hour; remove and rinse well.)
*Method:* Pre-mordant wool. Simmer twigs 1 hour; strain out twigs. Add wet pre-mordanted yarn to dyebath. Simmer 1 hour. Rinse well and hang weighted to dry if handspun.
   *Color:* Yellowish Brown 76, light yBr
*Lightfastness:* L5–6

*2. Dyestuff:* Black-eyed susan (*Rudbeckia* sp.), flowers
   *Ratio:* 4 quarts flowers covered with water in 3-gallon pot to produce 2 gallons of dye for approximately 4 ounces of yarn
*Mordant:* Dissolve 2 ounces of alum in 2 gallons of water. Add 4 ounces of wool; simmer 1 hour; remove and rinse well.
*Method:* Pre-mordant wool. Simmer flowers 1 hour; strain out limp flowers. Add wet pre-mordanted yarn to dyebath. Simmer 1 hour; remove. Rinse well and hang weighted to dry if handspun.
   *Color:* Greenish Yellow 105, grayish gY
*Lightfastness:* L3–4

*3. Dyestuff:* Black raspberries (*Rubus* sp.)
   Mary notes that she has her own berry bushes and the berries used for dye were not fit to eat; the dye smelled good, however!
   *Ratio:* 1 quart berries to approximately 4 ounces wool

*Mordant:* Dissolve 2 ounces alum, 1 ounce cream of tartar in 2 gallons of water. Add 4 ounces wetted wool yarn and simmer 1 hour. Remove and rinse.

*Method:* Crush berries in 1 gallon cold water. Bring to simmer and maintain for 1 hour. Strain out berries; add water to bring to 1 gallon. Add pre-mordanted yarn. Bring to simmer and maintain for 1 hour. Remove and rinse well; hang weighted to dry if hand-spun.

*Color:* Purplish Blue 199, light pB

*Lightfastness:* L3

*4. Dyestuff:* Milkweed (*Asclepias* sp.), blossoms
You might want to wear gloves if you pluck the blos-

*The milkweed (Asclepias syriaca), or butterfly weed, is a common plant. Some parts are edible. The plant produces yellow and brown dyes.* (Photo: Jan Cornies, courtesy Jones Sheep Farm)

soms with your hands, since the plant fluid stains and is quite sticky.

*Ratio:* 1 peck of blossoms to 4 ounces of yarn (Mary notes that a mill once processed some fleece for her and mixed in some polyester fibers with the wool. She has spun the fiber into yarn [90% wool, 10% polyester] and when it dyes, the polyester does not take the natural dyes. This results in a "frosted" appearance.)

*Mordant:* Mix 1/4 cup ammonia in 2 gallons water. Add 4 ounces yarn; bring to a simmer and maintain the temperature for 1 hour. Rinse well; air dry.

*Method:* Cover blossoms with water in 5-gallon container. Bring to simmer and maintain for 1 hour. Strain out dyestuff. Add pre-mordanted yarn. Bring to a simmer and maintain for 1 hour. Remove, rinse and dry.

77

*Color:* Neutral 263, white
*Lightfastness:* L6

**5. Dyestuff:** Sumac (*Rhus* sp.), leaves

Rhus typhina *(staghorn sumac) and other sumac species have traditionally provided drab dyes and an excellent source for tannic acid used in textile dyeing and leather tanning.* (Photo: Jan Cornies, courtesy Jones Sheep Farm)

*Ratio:* 1 peck of leaves to approximately 4 ounces of yarn
*Mordant:* None
*Method:* Simmer the leaves covered with water for 1 hour. Strain out leaves. Add wetted yarn. Bring to simmer and maintain for 1 hour. Rinse well; hang to air dry.
*Color:* Yellowish Brown 79, light grayish yBr (on 90% wool, 10% polyester)
*Lightfastness:* L6

**6. Dyestuff:** Sumac (*Rhus* sp.), berries
Gather the berries in the fall before hard frost.
*Ratio:* 1 peck of berry clusters to approximately 4 ounces yarn
*Mordant:* None
*Method:* Simmer berry clusters covered with water for 1 hour. Strain out berries. Add wetted yarn. Bring to simmer and maintain for 1 hour. Rinse well; hang to air dry.
*Color:* Yellowish Brown 79, light grayish yBr (on 90% wool, 10% polyester)
*Lightfastness:* L4–5

78

**7. Dyestuff:** Black walnuts and sumac berries *(Juglans nigra, Rhus sp.)*

**Ratio:** 1 peck black walnuts for bath 1; 1 peck sumac berries for bath 2; about 2 ounces of yarn for the testing

**Mordant:** Dissolve 1 ounce alum in 1 gallon water. Add yarn, bring to simmer and maintain 1 hour. Remove and rinse.

**Method:** Each dyebath was prepared as follows and the ooze was stored in a covered container in a cool, damp basement for over a year.

**Bath 1:** Cover black walnuts with water in a non-reactive pot. Bring to simmer and maintain for 1 hour. Strain out walnuts before storing the thick ooze.

**Bath 2:** Cover sumac berries with water in a non-reactive pot. Bring to simmer and maintain for 1 hour. Strain out berries before storing the ooze.

**To Dye:** Add mordanted yarn to bath 1. Bring to simmer and maintain for 1 hour. Remove and rinse. Add rinsed, walnut-dyed yarn to bath 2. Bring to simmer and maintain for 1 hour. Remove, rinse, and hang to air dry.

**Color:** Yellow 90, grayish Y

**Lightfastness:** L3–4

**8. Dyestuff:** Sassafras *(Sassafras albidum)*, root bark
This root is the base of many herbal teas as well as some root-beer concoctions. It has a pleasant odor of oranges and vanilla when cooking.

**Ratio:** 2 cups dry, peeled root bark to about 4 ounces wool

**Mordant:** *Color 1:* Dissolve 2 ounces alum and 1/2 ounce cream of tartar in 1 gallon water. Add 2 ounces wool yarn. Bring to simmer and maintain 1 hour. Remove and rinse well.
*Color 2:* Dissolve 2 ounces alum in 1 gallon water. Add 2 ounces wool yarn. Bring to simmer and maintain 1 hour. Remove and rinse yarn.

**Method:** Add 2 cups root bark to 1 gallon water in non-reactive pot. Bring to simmer and maintain for 1 hour. Strain out dyestuff; add water to make 1 gallon of dyebath. Add wetted yarn to dyebath; bring to simmer, and maintain for 1 hour. Remove, rinse, and hang yarn to air dry.

**Color 1:** Reddish Brown 42, light rBr

**Color 2:** Pink 7, pale Pk

**Lightfastness:** L4–5 (both samples tested at this level)

# *Marilyn Jones* | Kansas

Marilyn Jones and her husband own a sheep farm with about 250 breeding ewes, 20 spinning wheels, students who come each summer to spin and dye with natural materials, and a garden full of dye plants. Marilyn admits to having had no intention of ever dyeing, but she got bored looking at creamy fleeces and decided to put some fleece and plants in a dyepot. Here are some of the colorful results gleaned from measured amounts of mordants and always using a "potful" of dyestuff.

**1. Dyestuff:** Broomweed *(Gutierrezia sarothrae)*
**Method:** Pre-mordant wool (as below). Fill the pot with fresh plant; simmer 1 hour and strain out dyestuff. Add yarn and simmer 45 minutes. Remove and rinse yarn.
**Mordant:** 1 1/2 tablespoons alum dissolved in 1 gallon of water for each 4 ounces of wool. Simmer 45 minutes; remove and rinse.
**Color:** Yellow 84, strong Y
**Lightfastness:** L6
**Mordant:** For each 4 ounces of wool dissolve 1/2 teaspoon of chrome in 1 gallon of water. Simmer wool 45 minutes; remove and rinse.
**Color:** Brown 55, strong Br
**Lightfastness:** L6

**2. Dyestuff:** Goldenweed (*Grindelia* sp.)
**Method:** Pre-mordant wool (as below). Fill the pot with fresh plant; simmer 1 hour and strain out dyestuff. Add yarn and simmer 45 minutes. Remove and rinse yarn.
**Mordant:** For each 4 ounces of wool dissolve 1 1/2 tablespoons alum in 1 gallon of water. Simmer wool 45 minutes; remove and rinse.
**Color:** Yellow 89, pale Y
**Lightfastness:** L4–5
**Mordant:** For each 4 ounces of wool dissolve 1/2 teaspoon of chrome in 1 gallon of water. Simmer wool 45 minutes; remove and rinse.
**Color:** Yellow 87, moderate Y
**Lightfastness:** L4–5

**3. Dyestuff:** Indigo *(Indigofera tinctoria)*
**Method:** Into 1/2 gallon of warm water in a granite, enamel, or

80

stainless steel pan, stir 2 tablespoons powdered sodium carbonate (sal soda) until dissolved. Add one teaspoon powdered indigo. Slowly stir into this 2 tablespoons sodium hydrosulfite; add more if a coppery-colored scum has not formed on top in about 5 minutes. Let the bath stand in a warm place for about 1/2 hour to dissolve the indigo. Use as much of the mixture as is needed to produce the desired color. Enter the wet wool and stir constantly, taking care to keep the wool under the surface of the dyebath, and keep it in the dye for about 15 minutes. Lift the yarn and air it for 15 minutes. This will oxidize the indigo and cause the color to turn from a yellowish green to blue. The wool can be dipped again and again, with oxidation in between dippings for darker colors.

*Color:* Blue 189, bluish white (after a 2-minute dip)
*Lightfastness:* L6
*Color:* Blue 181, light B (after a 30-minute dip)
*Lightfastness:* L6

*4. Dyestuff:* Osage orange *(Maclura pomifera),* sawdust
The Indians of the Plains used to cherish bows and arrows made from the wood of this tree. In recent history it has had extensive planting as a windbreak tree across the Great Plains.
*Method:* Pre-mordant wool (as below). Fill the pot with the sawdust and cover with water; simmer 1 hour. Strain out dyestuff. Add yarn and simmer 45 minutes. Remove and rinse yarn.
*Mordant:* For each 4 ounces of wool dissolve 1 1/2 tablespoons alum in 1 gallon of water. Simmer yarn 45 minutes; remove and rinse.
*Color:* Yellow 85, deep Y
*Lightfastness:* L6
*Mordant:* For each 4 ounces of wool dissolve 1/2 teaspoon chrome in 1 gallon of water. Simmer yarn 45 minutes; remove and rinse.
*Color:* Olive Brown 94, light OlBr
*Lightfastness:* L6
*Mordant:* For each 4 ounces of wool dissolve 1 1/2 teaspoons copper in 1 gallon of water. See"Method" above.
*Color:* Brown 62, dark grayish Br
*Lightfastness:* L6

*Mordant:* Alum with short indigo afterbath. See "Method" above.
*Color:* Yellowish Green 137, dark yG
*Lightfastness:* L6
*Mordant:* Chrome with indigo overbath slightly longer than for the alum-mordanted yarn above
*Color:* Yellowish Green 138, very dark yG
*Lightfastness:* L6

*5. Dyestuff:* Smoke tree *(Cotinus coggygria)*
*Method:* Fill the pot with smoke tree twigs and leaves; cover plant with water and simmer 1 hour. Add pre-mordanted yarn (see below) and simmer 45 minutes. Remove yarn and rinse.
*Mordant:* For each 4 ounces of wool dissolve 1 1/2 tablespoons of alum in 1 gallon of water. Simmer yarn 45 minutes; remove and rinse.
*Color:* Yellowish Brown 76, light yBr
*Lightfastness:* L3–4
*Mordant:* For each 4 ounces of wool dissolve 1/2 teaspoon of chrome in 1 gallon of water. Simmer yarn 45 minutes; remove and rinse.
*Color:* Brownish Orange 54, brO
*Lightfastness:* L5
*Mordant:* For each 4 ounces of wool dissolve 1 1/2 teaspoons of copper in 1 gallon of water. Simmer yarn 45 minutes; remove and rinse.
*Color:* Brown 56, deep Br
*Lightfastness:* L5

# *Nancy & Janusz Kozikowski* | New Mexico

The traditions of weaving found in Janusz Kozikowski's native Poland and in the southwestern area of the United States where he and his wife Nancy live are carried on in their fiber work. They are weavers who utilize tapestry rug-weaving techniques with handspun and commercial wool yarns that are dyed with natural materials.

In their dyeing and weaving they thrive on spontaneity and improvisation within the limitations of traditional techniques and materials. Janusz feels that they are taking part in a continuing course in color theory as they work with subtle shades and the nuances of tone possible through accidental blending of colors. Their dye palette consists of locally available chamizo, cota, onion skins, marigolds, and black walnut hulls. They purchase indigo, cochineal, and brazil-wood to supplement the native colors. For strong, bold, highly contrasting colors they depend on a chrome mordanting process. Alum mordanting supplies softer, gentler pastels and brighter hues.

The Kozikowski team usually mordants spun or unspun wool in 5-pound lots in a 15-gallon container, following a usual measure of either 1 1/4 teaspoons chrome or about 4 tablespoons alum per pound of wool for the first batch of wool. Successive batches in the same bath get an extra 1 teaspoon of chrome or about 2–3 tablespoons of alum per pound of wool added to the pot. They mordant wool frequently in order to maintain a good stockpile of ready-to-dye wool. The mordanted wool is stored in a dark place until ready for use. A range of shades for their tapestry rugs is produced by dyeing several shades of white and gray wools, by adding skeins to the dye-pot at intervals, and by overdyeing. Here is their basic working method:

1. Mix and begin heating the mordant bath—to about 125–140° F (52–60° C).

2. Make the skeins and tie them loosely in four places.

3. In a washing machine, wash or wet the unspun wool or skeins to the same temperature as the mordant. Spin water out in the "damp dry" spin cycle; do not agitate as this may cause felting. (Nancy states that because of the quantities of wool with which they work it is important to speed drying, and the spin-dry cycle of the washing machine removes a large percentage of the water.)

4. Place the wool in the mordant bath.

5. Make the dye by placing the dyestuff in 4–5 gallon-size enamel pots with hot water. Dyestuff is not weighed, since it is the timing of the bath (not the amount of dyestuff used) that determines the sequence of colors. More dyestuff used means a stronger bath, however. Onion skins are tied in loose cheesecloth bundles; chamizo is chopped in 3-inch chunks to fill the pot 3/4 full; cota is broken up slightly to fill the pot 3/4 full.

6. Bring the dye to a boil; simmer 30–60 minutes and strain out the dyestuff.

7. Remove the desired amount of wool (usually 3 skeins) from the mordant bath, drain and place them in the dyebath. (Note: since only one mordant has been used on the wool going into the dyebath, it is not necessary to rinse the mordant. Rinsing well is necessary to prevent bleeding of mordants when materials pre-mordanted with more than one mordant are put into the same dyebath.)

8. Bring the dyepot to a boil and simmer 15–20 minutes.

9. Place the next group of skeins in the dyepot and continue adding skeins at 15-minute intervals until the dyepot is full.

10. Leave the wool in the dyepot overnight to cool for a deeper color.

11. Rinse the skeins in mild, soapy water, then in like temperature clear water in the washing machine; do not agitate. Spin the water out in the damp-dry spin cycle.

12. Dry yarn until ready for weaving.

Below are listed some of the color-range sequences obtained by Nancy and Janusz. You will note that some of the darker colors are also the most lightfast; the darker colors spent the most time in the dyebath.

*1. Dyestuff:* Black walnut *(Juglans nigra),* hulls

*Black walnut* (Juglans nigra) *is a dyer's favorite source of no-mordant needed brown dyes rich in depth of color.* (Photo: Jan Cornies, courtesy Jones Sheep Farm)

*Mordant:* None
*Color:* Brown 58, moderate Br
*Lightfastness:* L6
*Color:* Brown 56, deep Br.
*Lightfastness:* L6
*Color:* Brown 59, dark Br
*Lightfastness:* L6

*2. Dyestuff:* Cochineal *(Dactylopius coccus)*
*Mordant:* Alum
*Color:* Purplish Pink 249, light pPk

*Lightfastness:* L2–3
    *Color:* Purplish Red 262, grayish pR
*Lightfastness:* L2–3
    *Color:* Purplish Red 256, deep pR
*Lightfastness:* L4–5
    *Color:* Purplish Red 259, dark pR
*Lightfastness:* L5–6

    *3. Dyestuff:* Chamizo or rabbitbrush (*Chrysothamnus* spp.)
    *Mordant:* Chrome
    *Color:* Yellow 87, moderate Y
*Lightfastness:* L6
    *Color:* Yellow 85, deep Y
*Lightfastness:* L6
    *Color:* Yellowish Brown 74, strong yBr
*Lightfastness:* L6
    *Color:* Yellow 91, dark grayish Y (on naturally colored wool)
*Lightfastness:* L6
    *Color:* Olive Brown 95, moderate OlBr (on naturally colored wool)
*Lightfastness:* L6
    *Color:* Olive Brown 94, light OlBr
*Lightfastness:* L6

    *4. Dyestuff:* Cota (*Thelesperma* sp.)
    *Mordant:* Chrome
    *Color:* Yellowish Brown 79, light grayish yBr
*Lightfastness:* L6
    *Color:* Yellow 90, grayish Y
*Lightfastness:* L5–6
    *Color:* Brown 57, light Br
*Lightfastness:* L5–6
    *Color:* Brownish Orange 54, brO
*Lightfastness:* L5–6
    *Color:* Brown 55, strong Br
*Lightfastness:* L6
    *Color:* Brown between 55, strong Br, and 56, deep Br
*Lightfastness:* L6
    *Color:* Brown 56, deep Br (on colored wool)
*Lightfastness:* L6

    *5. Dyestuff:* Onion skins (*Allium* spp.)
    *Mordant:* Chrome

   *Color:* Yellowish Brown 79, light grayish yBr
*Lightfastness:* L5–6
   *Color:* Orange Yellow 72, dark OY
*Lightfastness:* L5–6
   *Color:* Orange Yellow 69, deep OY
*Lightfastness:* L5–6
   *Color:* Yellowish Brown 74, strong yBr
*Lightfastness:* L5–6
   *Color:* Brown 55, strong Br
*Lightfastness:* L5–6
   *Color:* Brown 58, moderate Br
*Lightfastness:* L5–6
   *Color:* Brown 56, deep Br
*Lightfastness:* L5–6

  *6. Dyestuff:* Brazilwood (*Caesalpinia* spp.)
  *Mordant:* Alum
   *Color:* Pink 4, light Pk
*Lightfastness:* L2–3
   *Color:* Red 12, strong Red
*Lightfastness:* L3–4
  *Mordant:* Chrome
   *Color:* Reddish Purple 240, light rP
*Lightfastness:* L2–3
   *Color:* Reddish Purple 244, pale rP
*Lightfastness:* L2–3
   *Color:* Reddish Purple 238, deep rP
*Lightfastness:* L3–4
   *Color:* Reddish Purple 243, very dark rP
*Lightfastness:* L5–6

# *Sue Lacey* | Colorado

When Sue Lacey's daughter came home with eight overripe papayas, Sue peeled the fruit, made jelly, and threw the peelings in the compost. She had second thoughts and removed the papaya skins from the heap and threw them in a pot of water. After all, she thought, how often does a Colorado resident have eight papaya skins at one time? That was Sue's first dyebath, and though it produced what Sue calls a "yukky" color, it was enough to encourage more experiments.

  Sue is an inveterate recycler, and not many plants leave her garden

*The author* (right) *is wearing a needle-woven overshirt of handspun wool dyed with onion skins and an alum mordant.*

*Linda Berry Walker* (below) *wears her handspun vegetal-dyed hat and poncho as she inspects her yearling Romney lambs which will provide next year's spinning and dyeing wool.*

*Wool fleece dyed by Fred Gerber from the* Umbilicaria mamulata *lichen it surrounds.* (Photo: Carmichael)

*Theresa Padgham collects lichens from rocks such as this one in northern Canada, where she works as a geologist. Her experiments use only the required amounts of lichens to test the color potential of the various arctic and subarctic lichen species.*

*Fred Gerber* (below) *examines some cochineal-infested prickly pear cacti* (Opuntia sp.) *in Florida. Cochineal insects feed upon the cacti. They derive and concentrate the carminic acid from the plant within their own body. The insects can thus be used as dyestuff to impart a range of reds and pinks —as seen in the yarns in the foreground.* (Photo: Carmichael)

*Mary Lou Wilcox's green redwood* (Sequoia sempervirens) *cones in the pot with dyeing wool.*

*Edith Marsh wears her "Indigo Sweater" while checking a sage plant near her home in eastern Washington.* (Photo: Betty Davenport)

*Linda Berry Walker dyed this assortment of wool- and hair-fiber yarns with natural dyes. They are commercially spun yarns.*

*"Sea Anemones"* (left) *by Judy Wallen of Baranof Island, Alaska. The crocheted piece is made entirely of naturally dyed wool, some of which is handspun.* (Photo: Sue Taylor)

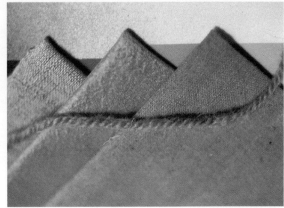

Above: *A selection of Junko Sato Pollack's purple-root–dyed silks, wool, and cotton/hemp—shown with the color chips from the Centroid Color Chart to which dyed colors can be compared.*

Below: *"Spring Shawl" (27" x 76") by Cheryl Kolander is woven of naturally dyed wools, brown alpaca, and white silk.* (Design copyright Cheryl Kolander, 1978)

*A spectrum assortment of yarns dyed naturally during one of Fred Gerber's workshops.*

Doris Beug displays her two naturally dyed afghans. The one on the left was crocheted from commercially spun yarns, and the one on the right was woven using her handspun wools. All yarns were dyed by Doris.

Above: *"Polish Cross #5" rug (29" x 72") woven of handspun naturally dyed wool yarns by Nancy Kozikowski.*

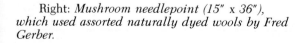

A detail of the *"Aspens"* tapestry by Sally Posner features only native plant-dyed wool yarns.

Right: *Mushroom needlepoint (15" x 36"), which used assorted naturally dyed wools by Fred Gerber.*

for points beyond without first being brewed for dye. She works with a basic method, a variety of mordants, and any plant that hints even vaguely at color production.

Sue usually pre-mordants clean wool yarn, either her fine handspun wool or mohair or commercially spun wools, by the following procedure:

1. For 1 pound of clean dry wool dissolve one of the following in a 4-gallon enamel pot of water: alum (4 tablespoons), chrome (3 teaspoons), copper (2 tablespoons), iron (2 tablespoons), or tin (2 teaspoons).
2. Add the clean yarn, well wetted, to the mordant bath.
3. Bring the temperature to a simmer and maintain for 1 hour.
4. Cool the yarn in the mordant bath overnight.
5. Remove and rinse thoroughly.

The plants below were used fresh in a 1:1 weight ratio with the clean, dry wool. They were simmered for 1 hour covered with water and left overnight in the bath to cool before straining out the dyestuff. The yarns were then entered into the bath, simmered 1 hour, and left to cool overnight in the bath before rinsing and drying.

*1. Dyestuff:* Comfrey *(Symphytum officinale),* leaves and stalks
*Mordant:* Tin
*Color:* Yellowish Pink 31, pale yPk
*Lightfastness:* L4–5

*2. Dyestuff:* Corcopsis (*Coreopsis* spp.), blossoms and stems
Its botanical name comes from its ability to tint or color. A traditional source of yellow dye, coreopsis is as popular now as ever, and is grown in many dyers' gardens.
*Mordant:* Alum
*Color:* Orange Yellow 69, deep OY
*Lightfastness:* L5–6

*3. Dyestuff:* Feverfew (*Anthemis* spp.), blossoms, leaves, and stalks
*Mordant:* Alum
*Color:* Greenish Yellow 104, pale gY
*Lightfastness:* L5–6

*4. Dyestuff:* Flax (*Linum* spp.), stems, leaves, and flowers
*Mordant:* Alum, second dyebath/first exhaust dyebath
*Color:* Yellow 92, yellowish white
*Lightfastness:* L6

**5. Dyestuff:** Guinella maple (*Acer* sp.), leaves and stems
**Mordant:** Alum
**Color:** Greenish Yellow 101, light gY
**Lightfastness:** L5–6

**6. Dyestuff:** Nasturtium (*Tropaeolum* sp.), leaves and flowers
**Mordant:** Alum
**Color:** Greenish Yellow 101, light gY
**Lightfastness:** L3–4

**7. Dyestuff:** Morning-glory (*Ipomoea* sp.), blue blossoms picked just after frost
**Mordant:** Alum
**Color:** Yellow 89, pale Y
**Lightfastness:** L5–6

# *Doris A. Lewis* | Oregon

One might term Doris A. Lewis an itinerant dyer, since she seems to reap color from nature whether she's at home or traveling. Her travels in the United States, Canada, and Great Britain have resulted in colorful memories, made all the more vivid by the materials she collected along the way for use in her dyepot later. To do this, Doris has assembled a collecting kit which she carries in the car. It contains the following articles:

1. Small food dryer (Doris's is 14″ × 14″ × 14″). This is used for drying or dehydrating plants at night. Sometimes overseas she uses newspaper near the back car window to absorb moisture while driving; the plants can also be taken indoors at night to dry near a heat source.

2. Large paper sacks for collecting dry plants.

3. Pillow cases for collecting large amounts or slightly damp plants.

4. Plastic bags for collecting very wet plants. Do not put mushrooms into plastic bags as they decompose rapidly in heat.

5. Plastic bags, preferably with locking tops, to be marked with identification and where collected on the outside. These should be carried separately from regular luggage to go through customs. Check customs regulations concerning plant importation with the customs department prior to overseas travel. In the United States this information is usually available at your local post office.

6. Sputum pan (as used in hospitals) to hold next to trees or rocks

for scraping lichens. The pan's curvature fits close to the curved surface of the trees.

7. Rubber gloves.

8. Small knife and a tablespoon with one side ground down for ease in scraping.

9. Masking tape and permanent marker for marking on bags.

10. Aluminum foil, to carry plants in the car. It can also be used to reflect heat from the sun to speed drying outdoors.

11. Small garden hand cultivator on an extension pole for reaching into trees.

12. Handwarmers.

13. Boots.

14. An assortment of cutting utensils such as scissors, shears, knives, and pruners. You can choose your own.

Doris pre-mordants her clean, skeined wool by simmering it for 1 hour and cooling it in the bath before rinsing. She uses the following amount of metal salts per pound of wool: 4 tablespoons alum, 3 teaspoons chrome, 2 tablespoons copper, 2 tablespoons iron, or 2 teaspoons tin. The dyeing is done with the plants, pre-mordanted wool, and water all simmered together in stainless steel pots.

**1. Dyestuff:** Cow parsnip or cow parsley *(Heracleum lanatum)*, flowers

**Ratio:** 1/2 cup dry flowers to 4 ounces of pre-mordanted dry wool in 4 gallons of water (Doris suggests a clothespin for your nose when you brew this.)

**Method:** Place flowers, water, and wool in the pot. Bring to simmer and maintain heat for 1 hour. Remove and rinse.

**Mordant:** Alum

**Color:** Greenish Yellow 98, brilliant gY

**Lightfastness:** L3

**Mordant:** Chrome

**Color:** Yellow 84, strong Y

**Lightfastness:** L3–4

**Mordant:** Tin

**Color:** Yellow 82, vivid Y

**Lightfastness:** L3–4

**2. Dyestuff:** Yellow flat tree lichen *(Cetraria canadensis)*

**Ratio:** 1 1/2 cups dry lichen to 4 ounces pre-mordanted wool in 2 gallons water

*Method:* Bring to simmer after immersing lichen and wool in the water. Maintain simmer for 1 hour; remove and rinse.
*Mordant:* None
*Color:* Greenish Yellow 98, brilliant gY
*Lightfastness:* Less than L2
*Mordant:* Alum
*Color:* Greenish Yellow 104, pale gY
*Lightfastness:* Less than L2
*Mordant:* Chrome
*Color:* Greenish Yellow 105, grayish gY
*Lightfastness:* L2–3
*Mordant:* Tin
*Color:* Greenish Yellow 104, pale gY
*Lightfastness:* Less than L2

*3. Dyestuff:* Indian paint fungus *(Echinodontium tinctorum)*
This fungus was once used by Northwest Indians for paint and dye.
*Ratio:* 1 cup dry fungus to 4 ounces pre-mordanted wool in 2 gallons water
*Method:* Bring to simmer and maintain simmer 1 hour after adding wool to the water with the fungus. Remove and rinse.
*Mordant:* None
*Color:* Yellowish Brown 76, light yBr
*Lightfastness:* L2
*Mordant:* Alum
*Color:* Yellowish Brown 76, light yBr
*Lightfastness:* L3
*Mordant:* Chrome
*Color:* Brown 57, light Br
*Lightfastness:* L3–4
*Mordant:* Tin
*Color:* Orange Yellow 73, pale OY
*Lightfastness:* Less than L2

*4. Dyestuff:* Mushrooms *(Hypomyces* spp.)
*Ratio:* 1 cup dry mushrooms, 4 ounces pre-mordanted wool, 2 gallons of water
*Method:* Add water, mushrooms, and wool to pot. Bring to simmer and maintain simmer 1 hour. Remove and rinse in an ammonia solution of 1/2 cup ammonia in 1 gallon water. Remove and rinse.

*Mordant:* None, ammonia rinse
*Color:* Pink 5, moderate Pk
*Lightfastness:* L2
*Mordant:* Alum, ammonia rinse
*Color:* Pink 5, moderate Pk
*Lightfastness:* L3
*Mordant:* Chrome, ammonia rinse
*Color:* Pink 8, grayish Pk
*Lightfastness:* L2–3
*Mordant:* Tin, ammonia rinse
*Color:* Pink 4, light Pk
*Lightfastness:* L2–3

# *Harry Linder* | Arizona

While Harry Linder is perhaps best known for his handspinning abilities, he is also quite adept at weaving and dyeing with his handspun as well as commercial yarns. Harry often freezes dyestuff during the spring, summer, and fall to use for winter dyeing, storing enough of each plant to comfortably fill a pot. He has learned that many plants will produce strong enough dyes to be used for more than one batch of yarn, and that the plants can be dried or frozen and still produce excellent dye results.

Using the regular simmering baths to pre-mordant and dye yarns is only one method Harry uses. He has also tried solar dyeing and layering dyestuff and yarn in a putrefaction method. His mordants are carefully measured on a metric (gram) scale. They are based on a percentage of the dry weight of the yarn. This method works particularly well for Harry's skeins of handspun yarn, since they may have different, non-standardized weights. Here are Harry's mordants and the percentages used:

| *Mordant* | *Multiply dry weight by* |
| --- | --- |
| Alum | .15 to .25 |
| Cream of tartar | .06 |
| | |
| Chrome | .02 to .04 |
| Cream of tartar | .03 |
| | |
| Tin | .04 to .06 |
| Cream of tartar | .02 |
| Oxalic acid | .01 |

91

| | |
|---|---|
| Copper | .01 to .04 |
| Cream of tartar | .03 |
| Iron | .04 to .06 |
| Cream of tartar | .10 to .12 |

Note that Harry consistently uses mordant assistants and that the percentage of the metal salts is variable. This is based on the density of the yarn; Harry uses the higher percentages of metal salts with heavier, more densely spun yarns.

**1. *Dyestuff:*** Dock (*Rumex* sp.), dried root
**        *Mordant:*** Alum/cream of tartar
**            *Color:*** Orange Yellow 72, dark OY
**    *Lightfastness:*** Turned red brown; no loss of L6 intensity

*Dock (*Rumex spp.*) provided Native Americans with yellow and black dyes, offered pioneers crossing the country spring greens and seed to grind in the fall for meal. It is an abundant and common "weed" that will be fun to put in your dyepot.* (Photo: Jan Cornies, courtesy Jones Sheep Farm)

**        *Mordant:*** Chrome/cream of tartar
**            *Color:*** Brown 57, light Br
**    *Lightfastness:*** Turned red brown; no loss of L6 intensity
**        *Mordant:*** Tin/cream of tartar/oxalic acid
**            *Color:*** Orange Yellow 70, light OY
**    *Lightfastness:*** Turned red brown; no loss of L6 intensity
**        *Mordant:*** Copper/cream of tartar
**            *Color:*** Olive Brown 94, light OlBr
**    *Lightfastness:*** Turned red brown; no loss of L6 intensity
**        *Mordant:*** None
**            *Bath:*** Second bath

           *Color:* Yellowish Brown 76, light yBr
*Lightfastness:* Turned red brown; no loss of L6 intensity
      *Mordant:* None
          *Bath:* Third bath
          *Color:* Brown 57, light Br
*Lightfastness:* Turned browner; no loss of L6 intensity


  **2. *Dyestuff:*** Alder (*Alnus* sp.), bark
      *Mordant:* None
          *Bath:* Second bath with 24 hours solar heat
          *Color:* Yellow 93, yellowish gray
*Lightfastness:* L5–6


  **3. *Dyestuff:*** Oak galls, dried
      *Mordant:* Alum
          *Color:* Yellow 89, pale Y
*Lightfastness:* L6
      *Mordant:* Chrome
          *Color:* Greenish Yellow 105, grayish gY
*Lightfastness:* L4–5
      *Mordant:* None
          *Color:* Yellowish Brown 75, deep yBr
*Lightfastness:* L6
      *Mordant:* None
          *Bath:* Second bath
          *Color:* Yellow 89, pale Y
*Lightfastness:* L6


  **4. *Dyestuff:*** Peach *(Prunus persica),* leaves
      *Mordant:* Tin/cream of tartar/oxalic acid
          *Color:* Yellow 86, light Y
*Lightfastness:* L2–3
      *Mordant:* Tin/cream of tartar/oxalic acid
      *Top Dye:* Indigo
          *Color:* Yellowish Green 131, strong yG
*Lightfastness:* L3
      *Mordant:* Tin/cream of tartar/oxalic acid
      *Top Dye:* Cochineal
          *Color:* Reddish Orange 35, strong rO
*Lightfastness:* L4–5


  **5. *Dyestuff:*** Cockleburs (*Xanthium* sp.), dried
      *Mordant:* Alum

       *Bath:* Boiled 2 hours
      *Color:* Orange Yellow 73, pale OY
 *Lightfastness:* L3
   *Mordant:* Chrome/copper/cream of tartar
      *Color:* Greenish Yellow 102, moderate gY
 *Lightfastness:* L4
   *Mordant:* Tin/cream of tartar/oxalic acid
      *Color:* Yellow 89, pale Y
 *Lightfastness:* L4

    *6. Dyestuff:* Purple plum (*Prunus* sp.), frozen leaves
   *Mordant:* Alum
      *Color:* Yellowish Brown 77, moderate yBr
 *Lightfastness:* L3–4
   *Mordant:* Alum/cream of tartar/copper
      *Color:* Yellow 88, dark Y
 *Lightfastness:* L6
   *Mordant:* Chrome/cream of tartar
      *Color:* Olive Brown 94, light OlBr
 *Lightfastness:* L5–6
   *Mordant:* Tin/cream of tartar/iron
      *Bath:* Third bath
      *Color:* Yellow 91, dark grayish Y
 *Lightfastness:* L5–6

    *7. Dyestuff:* Iris (*Iris* sp.), roots
   *Mordant:* Tin/cream of tartar/oxalic acid
      *Color:* Yellow 89, pale Y
 *Lightfastness:* L6
   *Mordant:* Iron/cream of tartar
      *Color:* Yellowish Brown 76, light yBr
 *Lightfastness:* L3–4

    *8. Dyestuff:* Juniper (*Juniperus* sp.), berries
   *Mordant:* Alum/cream of tartar in dyebath dyeing gray wool
      *Color:* Neutral 265, medium gray
 *Lightfastness:* L6

    *9. Dyestuff:* Prickly pear cactus (*Opuntia* sp.), ripe fruit
   *Mordant:* None
    *Method:* Ferment yarn 6 days in mashed fruit.
      *Color:* Purplish Red 256, deep pR
 *Lightfastness:* Less than L2

# *Edith Marsh* | Washington

Edith Marsh is a very pragmatic addict to dyeing who has learned that almost any plant will produce a dye with a bit of coaxing, but some are certainly more desirable than others. She feels that since nature in-

*Edith Marsh wears a jacket woven from handspun natural black/brown wool with a pattern of white yarn; it was dyed with dahlias and a chrome mordant.* (Photo: Betty Davenport)

cludes all colors, everything dyed using nature's produce can go together. Nothing clashes. Edith notes that the higher the ratio of plant to wool, the stronger the color.

Most often Edith pre-mordants her clean yarn in skeins which can then be dried and stored until needed. She pre-mordants by filling her pot with water, dissolving her mordant separately in a small amount of water, and then adding it to the pot and mixing it well. Then she adds her well-wetted, scoured wool and brings the bath to a simmer that she maintains for one hour. Occasionally she stirs the wool gently in the bath. After the hour's simmer, Edith removes the pot from the heat to cool to hand temperature, at which point she removes and rinses the wool in hand-temperature clear water.

For 1 pound of clean, dry wool Edith uses these basic amounts of mordants in 4 gallons of water in a non-corrosive pot:

> Alum: 6 tablespoons of alum plus 6 tablespoons cream of tartar
> Chrome: 1 tablespoon of chrome plus 2 tablespoons cream of tartar (optional)
> Copper: 2 2/3 tablespoons copper crystals plus 2 tablespoons cream of tartar (optional)

Edith also adds tin, oxalic acid, and iron to the dyebath to effect a color change. To do this, she removes the wool from the dyebath, dissolves the mordant in a small amount of water, adds it to the dyebath, and mixes thoroughly. The wool is then re-immersed and simmered for 20 minutes before removal and final rinsing. Here are the amounts of tin, oxalic acid, and iron used per pound of dry wool:

> Tin: 2 teaspoons
> Iron: 4 teaspoons
> Oxalic Acid: 2 teaspoons

Sometimes Edith rinses the dyed wool in either an ammonia or vinegar solution (1 teaspoon of ammonia or vinegar per quart of water).

To prepare the dyebath, approximately 1 pound of dyestuff per pound of wool is covered with water in a non-reactive pot, brought to a simmer, and maintained at that temperature for 1 hour. The dyestuff is then strained and additional water is added to make 4 gallons of dye.

Dyeing is done by adding the well-wetted, mordanted wool to the dyepot, bringing the bath to a simmer and holding it for an hour or until the desired color is reached. Occasionally Edith stirs the dyebath gently. When dyed, the wool is removed, rinsed, and dried.

*1. Dyestuff:* Cosmos diablo (*Cosmos* sp.)
*Mordant:* Alum
*Color:* Orange Yellow 67, brilliant OY
*Lightfastness:* L3
*Mordant:* Alum; tin after
*Color:* Orange 48, vivid O
*Lightfastness:* L3
*Mordant:* Alum; tin/oxalic acid after
*Color:* Orange 48, vivid O
*Lightfastness:* L3
*Mordant:* Alum; iron after
*Color:* Olive 106, light Ol
*Lightfastness:* L3–4
*Mordant:* Copper
*Color:* Olive Brown 94, light OlBr
*Lightfastness:* L6
*Mordant:* Chrome
*Color:* Orange 51, deep O
*Lightfastness:* L6

*2. Dyestuff:* Dahlia (*Dahlia* sp.), yellow flowers
*Mordant:* Alum
*Color:* Yellow 82, vivid Y

*Lightfastness:* L3–4
    *Mordant:* Alum; oxalic acid added after
       *Color:* Greenish Yellow 98, brilliant gY
*Lightfastness:* L4
    *Mordant:* Alum; tin after
       *Color:* Orange Yellow 66, vivid OY
*Lightfastness:* L5
    *Mordant:* Alum; iron after
       *Color:* Olive Brown 95, moderate OlBr
*Lightfastness:* L6
    *Mordant:* Copper
       *Color:* Orange Yellow 72, dark OY
*Lightfastness:* L5–6
    *Mordant:* Chrome
       *Color:* Reddish Brown 40, strong rBr
*Lightfastness:* L5–6

**3. *Dyestuff:*** Hopsage (*Grayia* sp.)
    *Mordant:* Alum
       *Color:* Yellow 86, light Y
*Lightfastness:* L6
    *Mordant:* Alum; tin after
       *Color:* Yellow 83, brilliant Y
*Lightfastness:* L3–4
    *Mordant:* Alum; iron after
       *Color:* Olive 107, moderate Ol
*Lightfastness:* L5
    *Mordant:* Alum; oxalic acid after
       *Color:* Yellow 89, pale Y
*Lightfastness:* L6
    *Mordant:* Alum; ammonia rinse
       *Color:* Yellow 84, strong Y
*Lightfastness:* L4
    *Mordant:* Chrome
       *Color:* Greenish Yellow 105, grayish gY
*Lightfastness:* L5–6
    *Mordant:* Copper
       *Color:* Yellow Green 119, light YG
*Lightfastness:* L6

**4. *Dyestuff:*** Weld *(Reseda luteola)*
            Edith grows this traditional dyestuff in her garden.
    *Mordant:* Alum

  *Color:* Greenish Yellow 104, pale gY
*Lightfastness:* L5–6
 *Mordant:* Alum; tin after
  *Color:* Greenish Yellow 97, vivid gY
*Lightfastness:* L5–6
 *Mordant:* Alum; iron after
  *Color:* Olive 106, light Ol
*Lightfastness:* L6
 *Mordant:* Alum; ammonia rinse
  *Color:* Greenish Yellow 98, brilliant gY
*Lightfastness:* L4–5
 *Mordant:* Chrome
  *Color:* Olive Brown 94, light OlBr
*Lightfastness:* L6
 *Mordant:* Copper
  *Color:* Greenish Yellow 99, strong gY
*Lightfastness:* L6

 **5. *Dyestuff:*** Nut sedge (*Cyperus* sp.)
 *Mordant:* Alum
  *Color:* Yellowish Pink 31, pale yPk
*Lightfastness:* L2
 *Mordant:* Alum; tin after
  *Color:* Orange Yellow 73, pale OY
*Lightfastness:* L2–3
 *Mordant:* Alum; iron after
  *Color:* Gray 10, pinkish gray
*Lightfastness:* L5–6
 *Mordant:* Alum; oxalic acid after
  *Color:* Brownish Pink 33, brPk
*Lightfastness:* L3–4
 *Mordant:* Alum; ammonia rinse
  *Color:* Yellow 89, pale Y
*Lightfastness:* L2–3
 *Mordant:* Chrome
  *Color:* Neutral 264, light gray
*Lightfastness:* L4–5
 *Mordant:* Copper
  *Color:* Greenish Yellow 105, grayish gY
*Lightfastness:* L5
 *Mordant:* Copper; ammonia rinse
  *Color:* Greenish Yellow 105, grayish gY
*Lightfastness:* L5

# *Joy Mills* | California

The almost magical qualities which result from gathering things from nature and brewing them for dye fascinate Joy Mills. The mild climate where she lives in the central coastal area of California allows her to reap a great variety of dyestuffs from her garden—from lemon tree leaves to the avocado leaves which smell like spice tea while the bath is in preparation. Joy especially enjoys dyeing with aromatic plants, which often leave a pleasant odor behind in the wool yarns she uses.

Joy uses both unmordanted and pre-mordanted yarns, and she experiments with synthetic yarns in her dyes, too. Pre-mordanting can be done using 4 gallons of water and the amounts of mordants below for each pound of clean dry wool. Simmer the yarn for 1 hour; remove and rinse it after the bath has cooled enough to handle it with rubber gloves on your hands. Here are some suggested mordant amounts per pound of dry wool:

> Alum: 3 ounces plus 1 ounce cream of tartar
> Chrome: 1/2 ounce
> Copper: 1 ounce
> Iron: 1/2 ounce
> Tin: 1/4–1/2 ounce

*1. Dyestuff:* Avocado *(Persea gratissima),* leaves
This tree, a native of the West Indies, is sometimes called alligator pear because of its scaly, pear-shaped fruit that resembles alligator hide. The seeds supposedly yield an indelible ink.
*Ratio:* Use 2 to 3 pounds of leaves to 1 pound of wool; Joy says you can also dye polyester with this dye.
*Method:* Chop the leaves in 2- to 3-inch pieces. Cover the leaves with water in an enamel pot and soak overnight. Bring the pot to a simmer and maintain the temperature about 2 hours or until the water is a "peachy brown" color. Cool leaves overnight in the bath. Strain out leaves and enter wetted fiber or yarn. Bring to a simmer and maintain temperature for 2 hours. Cool fiber overnight in the bath. Remove and rinse.
*Mordant:* None
*Color:* Reddish Brown 42, light rBr
*Lightfastness:* L3–4

*Mordant:* Alum
*Color:* Orange 53, moderate O
*Lightfastness:* L3–4
*Mordant:* Chrome
*Color:* Brown 57, light Br
*Lightfastness:* L3–4
*Mordant:* Copper
*Color:* Brown 58, moderate Br
*Lightfastness:* L3–4
*Mordant:* Iron
*Color:* Brown 64, brownish gray
*Lightfastness:* L3–4
*Mordant:* Tin
*Color:* Brownish Orange 54, brO
*Lightfastness:* L3–4

**2. Dyestuff:** Eucalyptus *(Eucalyptus cinerea),* pods and leaves
*Ratio:* 7:1 weight ratio of fresh dyestuff to fiber
Unmordanted yarn takes the dye well, as does some polyester in Joy's experience. Dry leaves can also be used with comparable results. There is a strong odor associated with cooking eucalyptus—dye outdoors or with good ventilation. Eucalyptus oils are ingredients in many menthol cold preparations.
*Method:* Place the dyestuff, fiber, and water to cover in an enamel pot. Heat to simmer and maintain 6 hours or longer. The colors develop slowly; be patient. The bath can be simmered the next day if the colors have not gone from the yellows to the oranges or browns possible. Cool fiber overnight in the bath before rinsing.
*Mordant:* None
*Color:* Brownish Orange 54, brO
*Lightfastness:* L5–6
*Mordant:* Alum
*Color:* Brown 55, strong Br
*Lightfastness:* L5–6
*Mordant:* Chrome
*Color:* Brown 62, dark grayish Br
*Lightfastness:* L5–6
*Mordant:* Copper
*Color:* Brown 56, deep Br
*Lightfastness:* L5–6
*Mordant:* Iron
*Color:* Brown 62, dark grayish Br

*Lightfastness:* L5–6
*Mordant:* Tin
*Color:* Brown 55, strong Br
*Lightfastness:* L5–6

**3. Dyestuff:** Silver dollar eucalyptus *(Eucalyptus polyanthemos),* leaves and pods
*Ratio:* Same as for *Eucalyptus cinerea,* above
*Method:* Same as for *Eucalyptus cinerea,* above
*Mordant:* Alum
*Color:* Orange 51, deep O
*Lightfastness:* L5–6
*Mordant:* Chrome
*Color:* Orange Yellow 69, deep OY
*Lightfastness:* L5–6
*Mordant:* Copper
*Color:* Brown 55, strong Br
*Lightfastness:* L5–6
*Mordant:* Iron
*Color:* Brownish Orange 54, brO
*Lightfastness:* L5–6
*Mordant:* Tin
*Color:* Yellowish Brown 74, strong yBr
*Lightfastness:* L5–6

**4. Dyestuff:** Pomegranate *(Punica granatum),* insides and seeds (no rinds)
*Ratio:* Use the insides and seeds from 36 pomegranates to 1 1/2 pounds unmordanted wool yarn
*Method:* Wear an apron; the fruit splatters and stains. Crush the pomegranate insides gently to release juice into an enamel pot. Enter yarn and add enough water to cover well; stir to mix thoroughly. Bring to a simmer; add 1/2 ounce tin. Simmer 3 hours. Cool yarn overnight in this dyebath, which will not be exhausted. Remove and rinse.
*Color:* Violet 210, light V
*Lightfastness:* L2–3

# Edith Nelson | Washington

While Edith Nelson admits to sometimes feeling like the Witch of Endor as she brews her dye, she is actually taking great pleasure in the transmission of colors from all sorts of plants onto her handspun wool

101

yarns. Edith likes to work with large enough quantities of materials to dye a pound of yarn at a time. She most often uses a ratio of about 1 bushel or 3 kilograms of dyestuff to 1 pound of wool; however, she also dyes smaller amounts when experimenting or for a special project. Edith primarily tries to dye light, bright colors, and she notes that the natural low-key harmonies found in natural dyes provide individual qualities of beauty and interest for each color while still blending into a subtle unit with any other colors she is able to obtain from nature.

*1. Dyestuff:* Alder (*Alnus* sp.), bark
*Ratio:* 10 pounds bark to 8 ounces dry, clean wool yarn
*Mordant:* Mix 1 ounce alum in 3–4 gallons water to dissolve well. Add wetted yarn. Bring to simmer and maintain 1 hour. Cool yarn in mordant bath. Remove and rinse.
*Method:* Soak bark 1 day in water to cover in enamel pot. Add mordanted yarn to the bark-water. Bring to a boil and maintain for 2 hours. Remove and rinse.
*Color:* Yellow 89, pale Y
*Lightfastness:* L6

*2. Dyestuff:* Black birch (*Salix* sp.), bark
*Ratio:* 8 ounces chopped bark to 8 ounces clean, dry wool
*Mordant:* Mix 1 1/3 ounces alum into 3–4 gallons of water; stir to dissolve. Add wetted yarn. Bring to simmer and maintain 1 hour. Cool yarn in mordant bath. Remove and rinse.
*Method:* Soak bark chips for 1 day in water to cover in enamel pot. Boil bark and water for 2 hours. Strain out bark. Add wetted, mordanted yarn. Boil 1 hour or until the desired color is reached. Remove and rinse.
*Color:* Brown 58, moderate Br
*Lightfastness:* L6

*3. Dyestuff:* Goldenrod (*Solidago* sp.), blossoms
*Ratio:* 6 pounds flower heads to 8 ounces dry, clean wool
*Method:* Pre-mordant wool (as below). Place flower heads in cold water to cover in enamel pot. Bring to boil and maintain 1 hour. Strain out dyestuff. Add mordanted yarn. Bring to a boil and maintain 1 hour or until the desired color is reached. Remove and rinse.
*Mordant:* Alum
(Mix 2 1/2 ounces alum in 3–4 gallons of water per pound of wool in enamel pot; stir to dissolve. Add clean,

wetted yarn and heat to simmer. Simmer 1 hour and cool yarn in bath. Remove and rinse.)

*Color:* Greenish Yellow 98, brilliant gY

*Lightfastness:* L3–4

*Mordant:* Alum/chrome

(Mix 2 1/2 ounces alum and 1 ounce chrome in 3–4 gallons of water for each pound of wool in an enamel pot; stir to dissolve. Add clean wetted yarn and heat to simmer. Simmer 1 hour and cool yarn in bath. Remove and rinse.)

*Color:* Yellow 84, strong Y

*Lightfastness:* L3–4

**4. *Dyestuff:*** Jim Hill mustard or tumble mustard *(Sisymbrium altissimum)*

*Ratio:* 1 bushel chopped fresh mustard to 1 pound of clean, dry wool

*Mordant:* Mix 2 1/2 ounces alum in 3–4 gallons of water in an enamel pot per pound of wool. Add wetted wool, bring to simmer and maintain 1 hour. Cool yarn in bath. Remove and rinse.

*Post-Mordant:* Mix 1 ounce copper in 3–4 gallons water per pound of wool. Add dyed yarn. Bring to simmer and maintain 15–30 minutes or until reaching the desired color. Remove and rinse.

*Method:* Pre-mordant yarn. Cover chopped mustard with water in large pot. Boil 1 hour and strain out dyestuff. Add mordanted yarn. Bring to boil and maintain 1 hour. Remove and rinse. Add dyed yarn to post-mordant copper bath.

*Color:* Green 150, grayish G (note: this beautiful turquoise green resembles many indigo overdyed yellow shades)

*Lightfastness:* L3

**5. *Dyestuff:*** Oregon holly grape *(Mahonia* sp.), berries

*Ratio:* 3 quarts berries to 1 pound clean, dry wool

*Mordant:* Per pound of wool use 2 1/2 ounces alum, 1 ounce chrome, and 1/2 cup vinegar. Mix alum in 3–4 gallons of water in enamel pot. Add wool, bring to boil, and maintain 1 hour. Cool yarn in bath; remove and rinse.

*Method:* Mash berries in 3–4 gallons water in enamel pot. Add alum-mordanted wool to bath with chrome and vinegar, making certain to dissolve chrome or splotchy color will result. Boil 1 hour or until desired color is reached. Remove and rinse.

*Color:* Purple 228, grayish P
*Lightfastness:* L3–4
*Ratio:* 2 quarts berries per pound of wool
*Mordant:* Same as above with 3 quarts berries
*Method:* Same as above with 3 quarts berries
*Color:* Purple 227, pale P
*Lightfastness:* L3–4

*6. Dyestuff:* Plantain (*Plantago* spp.)
*Ratio:* 1 bushel fresh plantain per pound of clean, dry wool
*Mordant:* Mix 2 1/2 ounces alum, 1 ounce chrome, and 1 ounce copper per pound of wool in 3–4 gallons of water in an enamel pot. Add wetted yarn and simmer 1 hour. Cool yarn in bath; remove and rinse.
*Method:* Pre-mordant yarn. Cover plantain with water in large pot. Boil 1 hour and then strain out dyestuff. Add mordanted, wetted yarn and boil 1 hour or until reaching the desired color. Remove and rinse.
*Color:* Yellow Green 122, grayish YG
*Lightfastness:* L6

*7. Dyestuff:* Ponderosa pine *(Pinus ponderosa),* bark
Edith reports color variation for each dyelot; the colors are similar to madder red.
*Ratio:* 1 bushel chipped bark per pound of wool
*Mordant:* Dissolve 1 ounce of chrome in 3–4 gallons of water per pound of wool. Boil yarn in bath 1 hour. Cool yarn in bath; remove and rinse.
*Method:* Pre-mordant yarn. Soak bark chips in water to cover for 1 week in enamel pot. Boil bark chips for 1–2 hours; strain out chips. Add yarn and boil 1 hour or until reaching the desired color. Remove and rinse.
*Color:* Reddish Orange 38, dark rO
*Lightfastness:* L2–3

*8. Dyestuff:* Wild currant (*Ribes* sp.), stems and leaves
*Ratio:* 1 bushel of stems and leaves per pound of wool
*Mordant:* 2 1/2 ounces alum and 2 ounces copper per pound of clean, dry wool
(Dissolve alum in 3–4 gallons of water in enamel pot. Add wool and simmer 1 hour. Cool wool in bath; remove and rinse.)

*Method:* Boil dyestuff for 1 hour in water to cover. Strain out dyestuff. Add alum-mordanted wool and boil 1 hour. Add the 2 ounces of copper and boil the bath with the dyeing yarn 30–60 minutes more or until reaching the desired color.

*Color:* Olive Green 125, moderate OlGr

*Lightfastness:* L5

*Pat Ollivier with one of the babies who will provide next year's wool for spinning. Her poncho was dyed with marigolds and sagebrush.* (Photo: Betty Davenport)

*Indian paint fungus and the wool yarn Pat Ollivier dyed with it.* (Photo: Betty Davenport)

105

# Pat Ollivier | Washington

Pat Ollivier lives on an old farm in eastern Washington where she raises her own sheep to produce wool for her handspinning. She admits to trying to dye with everything she can get her hands on, including native woods and the lichens and fungi which grow on them. One of her favorite dyestuffs is the fungus *Echinodontium tinctorum.* It is commonly known as Indian paint fungus, and it was a source of color for native peoples living in Washington. Pat's ammonia fermentation method differs from the water-bath method elsewhere discussed for this fungus, and while her colors faded somewhat, they were very intense prior to testing in the weatherometer. The colors are very similar to those from Ponderosa pine bark (on which the fungus grows) and to red browns from madder.

> *Dyestuff:* Indian paint fungus *(Echinodontium tinctorum)*
> *Ratio:* 1:1 weight of fungus to dry, clean wool
> *Method:* Ferment the fungus covered with an ammonia solution made of 2 parts ammonia to 1 part water. Pat has found that a 2- to 3-day fermentation seems to work as well as 30 days of fermenting the fungus. Simmer pre-mordanted wool in the fermented dye liquor until the desired color is obtained.
> *Mordant:* Alum (3 ounces to 1 pound of wool is satisfactory)
> *Color:* Brownish Orange 54, brO
> *Lightfastness:* L3
> *Mordant:* Chrome (1/2 to 3/4 ounces to 1 pound of wool is satisfactory)
> *Color:* Reddish Brown 40, strong rBr
> *Lightfastness:* L4–5

# Martha Omer | Florida

One might consider Martha Omer a "born again" natural dyer, since she was a firm believer in and user of synthetic dyes for a long while. She was highly skeptical of obtaining viable dyes from plants. An active convert, Martha now owns bushels of naturally dyed yarns and hundreds of samples of colors produced from plants growing in her area—both undomesticated ones and those gleaned from friendly gardeners.

Martha pre-mordants clean wool yarn by the pound using alum

(4 tablespoons), chrome (3 teaspoons), copper (2 tablespoons), or tin (1 teaspoon) in a simmering water bath for 1 hour. Yarns are cooled in the mordant bath, dried out of direct sunlight, and stored in paper bags, ready to go.

The plants (normally in a 1:1 weight ratio with the dry fiber) are gathered, put into the dyepot with water to cover, and simmered about 30 minutes. At this point the warmed and well-wetted yarn is entered with the plants and pushed deep into the pot. Martha then simmers the bath, checking the yarn for color at 20-minute intervals with removal usually after 40 minutes of simmering. The yarn may, however, simmer as long as 2 hours or more before removal, or get left overnight in the bath to cool. Martha alters the pH by her personal "intuition" method, using vinegar, oxalic acid, ammonia, or soda in an amount that causes the color to shift.

Her file cards have extensive notes about the plants and the dye methods, and samples are attached for the results. An experimenter, Martha has found that dyeing with 20–24" lengths of yarn cut from the pre-mordanted skeins allows her to sample the color before dyeing in the larger quantities she uses for her weaving. A system of knots (alum gets a loose knot in the center of the length of yarn, chrome is doubled and knotted at the end, copper gets two knots at one end, tin has no knots) enables her to keep track of the yarn pieces in the dyepots.

Although Martha's area of the country has plants available for dyes all year round, she prefers to dye in two seasons—the spring and early summer (April through June) and the late fall (September to early December). She seems to find more greenish yellows produced in the spring and more golds and rusts in the fall.

*1. Dyestuff:* Bur marigold *(Bidens laevis)*
  *Mordant:* Alum
    *Color:* Orange 50, strong O
*Lightfastness:* L6
  *Mordant:* Alum; ammonia
    *Color:* Reddish Brown 43, moderate rBr
*Lightfastness:* L6
  *Mordant:* Chrome
    *Color:* Reddish Brown 43, moderate rBr
*Lightfastness:* L6
  *Mordant:* Chrome; ammonia
    *Color:* Reddish Orange 34, vivid rO
*Lightfastness:* L6
  *Mordant:* Tin

*Color:* Orange Yellow 72, dark OY
*Lightfastness:* L6

**2. Dyestuff:** Bur marigold *(Bidens mitis)*
  *Mordant:* Alum
  *Color:* Brown 55, strong Br
*Lightfastness:* L6
  *Mordant:* Chrome
  *Color:* Reddish Brown 43, moderate rBr
*Lightfastness:* L6
  *Mordant:* Tin
  *Color:* Yellowish Brown 74, strong yBr
*Lightfastness:* L5

**3. Dyestuff:** Coreopsis *(Coreopsis longiafolia)*
  *Mordant:* Alum
  *Color:* Brownish Orange 54, brO
*Lightfastness:* L6
  *Mordant:* Alum; copper
  *Color:* Brown 58, moderate Br
*Lightfastness:* L6
  *Mordant:* Chrome; copper
  *Color:* Brown 56, deep Br
*Lightfastness:* L6
  *Mordant:* Tin
  *Color:* Yellow 84, strong Y
*Lightfastness:* L6

**4. Dyestuff:** Air potato *(Dioscorea bulbifera)*
This is a nuisance vine with poisonous air tubers.
  *Mordant:* Alum
  *Color:* Yellow 87, moderate Y
*Lightfastness:* L6
  *Mordant:* Alum; tin afterbath
  *Color:* Yellow 85, deep Y
*Lightfastness:* L6
  *Mordant:* Chrome
  *Color:* Brown 55, strong Br
*Lightfastness:* L5–6
  *Mordant:* Chrome; tin afterbath
  *Color:* Olive Brown 94, light OlBr
*Lightfastness:* L6
  *Mordant:* Chrome; iron

*Color:* Olive Brown 96, dark OlBr
*Lightfastness:* L6
*Mordant:* Chrome; copper
*Color:* Olive Brown 95, moderate OlBr
*Lightfastness:* L6

**5. *Dyestuff:*** Saltbush *(Baccharis halimifolia)*
*Mordant:* Alum
*Color:* Greenish Yellow 104, pale gY
*Lightfastness:* L2–3
*Mordant:* Alum; tin
*Color:* Greenish Yellow 101, light gY
*Lightfastness:* L3–4
*Mordant:* Chrome
*Color:* Yellow 88, dark Y
*Lightfastness:* L3–4

# *Theresa Padgham* | Canada

Through her work as a geologist, Theresa Padgham has discovered the world of tiny plants which often grow on rocks and soil. Her dye experiments are with lichens found in the subarctic regions of northern Canada as well as with herbaceous plants. Lichens, however, have become her special interest and the source of a wide range of colors. Some of the lichens' own colors are such pale, delicate, neutral earth tones it is difficult to believe they have the potential to produce rich reds, tawny golds, and chocolate browns—but Theresa has discovered and unlocked their secrets.

Theresa rarely uses mordants, although many lichens do respond to color modification if mordants are used. Rather, she usually begins with a ratio of at least 2:1 (dry lichen weight to dry wool weight). This produces a strong dyebath, and by varying the length of time a series of skeins spends in the dyebath, a range of colors is obtained. The same bath can often be reused several times—subsequent colors becoming more and more pale.

To prepare a simmering water bath, Theresa adds her wool yarn to a water/vinegar bath to which the lichens have been added. She uses a ratio of about 1–3 teaspoons of vinegar per quart of water to each 2 ounces of well-dried lichens and 1–2 ounces of dry clean wool. This wool-lichen-vinegar/water bath is then simmered for the length of time it takes to obtain the desired color. The wool is then removed, rinsed, and dried. Sometimes the yarn is only soaked with the lichens in the vinegar solution, but Theresa reports an improvement in the color with simmering, particularly with the orchil or purple-producing lichens. She has found that some orchil lichens will dye more than five times their weight in wool.

**1. *Dyestuff:*** *Cornicularia divergens*
This lichen is universal on the boggy ground of arctic barrens, often mixed with other lichens in tangled, hairy mats. Specimens tested were collected near the community of Baker Lake, Northwest Territories.
***Ratio:*** 2 ounces dry lichen : 24 ounces water : 2 teaspoons vinegar : .45 ounce wool (3 skeins of .15 ounce each)
***Method:*** One-pot simmer with color variations at timed intervals
***Color:*** After 15 minutes—Orange Yellow 72, dark OY
***Color:*** After 2 hours—Yellowish Brown 74, strong yBr
***Color:*** After 12 hours—Yellowish Brown 75, deep yBr
***Lightfastness:*** L5–6, all samples

**2. *Dyestuff:*** *Asahinea chrysantha*
This lichen resembles frilly clumps as it grows in rock crevices with some soil. The specimens tested were collected near Takijug Lake, Northwest Territories.
***Ratio:*** 1 ounce dry lichen : 32 ounces water : 3 teaspoons vinegar : .30 ounce wool
***Method:*** One-pot simmer with color variations at timed intervals
***Color:*** After 1 hour—Yellowish Brown 76, light yBr
***Color:*** After 8 hours—Yellowish Brown 78, dark yBr
***Lightfastness:*** L5, both samples

**3. *Dyestuff:*** *Dactylina arctica*
This lichen grows on the ground in clumps resembling hands, and it is common throughout the arctic barrens. Specimens tested were collected near Takijug Lake, Northwest Territories.
***Ratio:*** .5 ounce lichen : 24 ounces water : 1 teaspoon vinegar : .15 ounce wool
***Method:*** One-pot simmer for 8 hours
***Color:*** Yellow 87, moderate Y
***Lightfastness:*** L4

**4. *Dyestuff:*** *Haematomma lapponicum*
This lichen grows like a crust on rocks. Specimens tested were collected at 66°07′ N and 112°18′ W—about

220 miles north of Yellowknife, Northwest Territories.

*Ratio:* 8 ounces well-dried lichen : 24 ounces water : 24 ounces ammonia : 6 skeins wool yarn of .15 ounce each

*Method:* Place lichen, water, and ammonia in a glass jar; close the lid and allow to ferment. Stir solution three times daily; it will be ready for use after 17 days of fermentation. Some colors are obtained by soaking at room temperature, others by simmering or top-dying (putting the already-dyed yarn into a second dyebath).

*Bath:* Soak 2 hours at room temperature

*Color:* Purplish Red 262, grayish pR

*Lightfastness:* L2

*Bath:* Soak 24 hours at room temperature

*Color:* Purplish Red 259, dark pR

*Lightfastness:* L2

*Bath:* Soak 24 hours at room temperature. Simmer an hour; then simmer in second dyebath in *Asahinea chrysantha* solution.

*Color:* Reddish Brown 44, dark rBr

*Lightfastness:* L5–6

*Bath:* Simmer 1 hour

*Color:* Purplish Red 259, dark pR

*Lightfastness:* L4–5

*Bath:* Simmer 8 hours

*Color:* Purplish Red 257, very deep pR

*Lightfastness:* L5

*Bath:* Simmer 8 hours; then simmer in second dyebath in *Asahinea chrysantha* solution.

*Color:* Reddish Brown 44, dark rBr

*Lightfastness:* L5


*5. Dyestuff:* *Thamnolia vermicularis*

This common whitish lichen grows on the ground in subarctic forests and barrens. Specimens tested were collected at 63°58′ N and 111°14′ W at McKay Lake, 150 miles north of Yellowknife, Northwest Territories.

*Ratio:* 1 ounce lichen : 24 ounces water : 3 teaspoons vinegar : .15 ounce wool

*Method:* One-pot simmer for 2 hours

*Color:* Greenish Yellow 101, light gY

*Lightfastness:* L3

# *Ruth Pierce* | Texas

Ruth Pierce's search for madder seeds and her experiences in propagating this historical dyeplant in various parts of Texas are nearly as remarkable as her efforts to preserve two historic buildings in the small coastal town of Blessing, Texas. The Blessing Historical Foundation now sells madder seeds produced by the plants Ruth grows in her garden of traditional and historically important dye plants.

Madder was reported growing near Rome by Pliny the Elder in the first century A.D. In America Thomas Jefferson and Dolly Madison encouraged growing it as a commercial crop because its red dye colors were so popular. Ruth tried seeds from Switzerland and from several American sources while learning about needed soils, sunlight, and water. She has found that in some cool, moist climates the madder plants will not set seeds and must be started from root transplants. They do, however, grow quite well in hotter and drier areas, and many dyers now grow their own madder (including Marilyn Jones in her Kansas garden, whose work was described earlier in this chapter).

Ruth's personal motivation for raising her own dyestuff is closely linked with her relationship to her environment and her keen interest in preserving the past and fostering it to enrich the tapestry of modern living. She is a lover of wildflowers, and she enjoys using nature's colors in any way she can.

Ruth pre-mordants her yarn with alum (3 ounces per pound of dry wool plus 1 ounce of cream of tartar) in a 4-gallon water bath brought slowly to a boil over a 30-minute period. The bath is kept at a simmer for 45 minutes. The first sample listed was dyed on commercially spun wool; the second used Ruth's own handspun wool. There was a slight amount of fading at the 80-hour exposure time, but much color remained in the intensely red orange/brown colors that resulted.

*Madder* (Rubia tinctorum) *will provide a traditional range of reds from the spreading rootstock.* (Photo: Jan Cornies, courtesy Jones Sheep Farm)

 *Dyestuff:* Madder *(Rubia tinctorum),* roots (dried and ground)
  *Ratio:* 8 ounces powdered root to 1 pound dry wool to 4 gallons of water in a non-reactive pot
 *Method:* Soak powdered root in water overnight. Put bath on to heat very slowly. Enter well-wetted wool when bath is lukewarm. Heat bath to a simmer and maintain. If it boils, the color will be brown rather than the hoped-for red oranges or red browns. Stir frequently during dyeing. Remove yarn when the color reaches the desired shade or after 1 hour of simmering; you can also allow the yarn to cool in the bath.
  *Bath:* First bath on commercial wool yarn
  *Color:* Red 11, vivid R
*Lightfastness:* L4–5
  *Bath:* Second bath on handspun wool yarn
  *Color:* Reddish Brown 43, moderate rBr
*Lightfastness:* L4

# *Sally Posner* | California

Sally Posner's background as a painter and her love of the plants that grow in the mountainous area of northeastern California where she lives easily led her to the colors she found were possible to obtain from nature. She found herself cooking up dyes to color her handspun wools using the wild elderberries her family didn't want to eat and the lichens falling off the winter's supply of wood. Sally is a dyer and a weaver, and she uses only colors from nature for her rugs and tapestries. Additionally, she uses only the vegetation found nearby, not imported dyestuffs.

 Sally's method is easily accomplished, and she uses it with the various groups of children and adults she instructs. She uses mordants before or during the dyeing process, and she does not worry about exact amounts or exact colors, since eventually they all find a place in her woven textiles.

 Here are Sally's basic amounts used for dyeing with natural materials, as well as her method. It's simple, easy to fit into any schedule, and works to produce beautiful colors.

 For each pound weight of dry, clean wool yarn use:

 *Mordant:* 1/4 cup alum or
    1 teaspoon tin or
    2 tablespoons chrome or
    2 tablespoons copper

Water: 1 large canning kettle full
Dyestuff: 1 large shopping bag full
Heat: Simmer with the lid on.
Time: Watch for the desired color; remove the yarn when you like it. There is no set time limit.

*1. Dyestuff:* Elderberry (*Sambucus* sp.), ripe fruit
*Mordant:* Alum
*Color:* Purplish Red 261, light grayish pR
*Lightfastness:* L3
*Mordant:* Copper
*Color:* Purplish Blue 204, grayish pB
*Lightfastness:* L2–3

*2. Dyestuff:* Shasta daisy (*Erigeron* sp.), leaves
*Mordant:* Copper
*Color:* Greenish Yellow 103, dark gY
*Lightfastness:* L5–6

*3. Dyestuff:* Black oak (*Quercus* sp.), bark
*Mordant:* Copper
*Color:* Olive 112, light Ol gray
*Lightfastness:* L5

*4. Dyestuff:* Black poplar (*Populus* sp.), leaves
*Mordant:* Copper (on gray wool)
*Color:* Olive 107, moderate Ol (yarn has a "heather" look)
*Lightfastness:* L6

*5. Dock* (*Rumex* sp.), herbaceous parts
*Mordant:* Chrome
*Color:* Greenish Yellow 102, moderate gY
*Lightfastness:* L5–6

# *Ada Townsend* | Kansas

Ada Townsend's dye sessions usually begin with what she terms "road-siding"—an early morning adventure in old clothes to reach roadside foraging areas not yet paved over by the developers of suburbs and shopping centers. In the back of her old Corvair she always carries pruning shears, a small shovel, a trowel, and paper sacks for collecting. Ada knows that weeds are special creations made just for dyers, and she collects them in abundance. Plants are gathered according to the season, and are brewed in enamel corn-cooking pots to color the worsted wool yarns she uses in her knitting projects.

Ada's usual working procedures involve pre-mordanting with alum (3 ounces alum plus 1 ounce cream of tartar to 1 pound of clean, dry wool simmered 1 hour in 4 gallons of water) or chrome (1/2 ounce chrome per pound of clean, dry wool simmered 1 hour in 4 gallons of water). She adds tin (a pinch per quart of water), copper (1/4 teaspoon per pound of clean, dry wool), or iron (a pinch per quart of water) to the dyebath to alter colors. Dyestuffs can be variable in amount, but a 1:1 ratio is good for a starter, and the higher the ratio of plant to fiber, the stronger will be the dyebath.

Although Ada's forte is the native plants of her area, she also tries dyestuffs from across the country. Experiments with lichen (staghorn moss, *Evernia* sp.) from near Lake Tahoe in California have produced a vibrant range of yellows and greens while giving a pleasant and long-lasting scent to the wool.

> *Dyestuff:* Staghorn moss (*Evernia* sp.), dry lichens
> *Method:* Fill the pot with lichen and simmer covered with water for 1 hour. Add alum–pre-mordanted yarn, and simmer to the desired color. Remove and rinse. Add chrome, copper, or tin as previously described and stir thoroughly to dissolve. Re-enter the dyed yarn, or a portion of it, and simmer until the desired color change occurs.
> *Mordant:* Alum
> *Color:* Greenish Yellow 98, brilliant gY
> *Lightfastness:* L2–3
> *Mordant:* Copper
> *Color:* Yellow Green 116, brilliant YG
> *Lightfastness:* L4–5
> *Mordant:* Chrome and tin
> *Color:* Greenish Yellow 97, vivid gY
> *Lightfastness:* L4–5

# *Judy Wallen* | Alaska

Judy Wallen lives in a non-electrified rural area on Baranof Island off the coast of southeastern Alaska. Her lifestyle easily accommodates walks through the rainforest, along the beach, or over the old boardwalks in search of materials to use as dyes for the yarns she uses in her weaving, crocheting, and knitting. Her dyeing has led Judy into botany and plant identification, exploration of plants in her area as herbs, and discoveries of new wild plants to eat. She feels that all these things seem to fit together in her life. Judy's dye methods involve very little exact measurement, since she prefers the variety and serendipity afforded by each pot of dye, and does not attempt to duplicate dyes.

Yarn is usually pre-mordanted using about 3 ounces of alum plus 1 ounce of cream of tartar in 4 gallons of water for each pound of clean, dry wool. She also pre-mordants with copper, using about 1 tablespoon per pound of wool. Yarn is simmered in the mordant bath for about an hour before the yarn is removed and rinsed.

To prepare the dyebaths, Judy boils her dyestuff on the back of her oil stove for 1–2 hours before straining out the material. The bath is let cool to lukewarm. The pre-mordanted yarn is then put into the lukewarm dyebath and heated to a simmer which is maintained until the desired color is obtained. Judy then removes the yarn, lets it cool to lukewarm, and rinses it until the water runs clear. Excess water is gently squeezed out; then the yarn is rolled in a towel to absorb more moisture before complete drying (out of sun light).

*Judy Wallen collects species of* Parmelia *lichen from under the boardwalk to brew her "boardwalk brown."* (Photo: Sue Taylor)

*1. Dyestuff:* Wild blueberries (*Vaccinium* sp.), ripe berries
The two colors were obtained at separate times from separate baths; note the color difference.
*Mordant:* Alum
*Color:* Red 18, light grayish R
*Lightfastness:* L3
*Mordant:* Alum
*Color:* Red 23, dark reddish gray
*Lightfastness:* L3

116

**2. Dyestuff:** Horsetail or scouring rush (*Equisetum* sp.), young shoots collected in spring
**Mordant:** Alum
**Color:** Greenish Yellow 101, light gY
**Lightfastness:** L4 (also browned slightly)

**3. Dyestuff:** Lungwort *(Lobaria pulmonaria),* collected from rocks and hemlock trees
**Mordant:** None
**Method:** Tie lichen in an old nylon stocking; place in dyepot, and cover with water. Soak overnight. Add yarn to bath and simmer to desired color.
**Color:** Yellowish Brown 77, moderate yBr
**Lightfastness:** L4–5

**4. Dyestuff:** Lichen (*Parmelia* spp.)
These lichens produce many varied shades of what Judy terms her "boardwalk browns," since the lichens are collected from the boardwalks where they grow abundantly.
**Mordant:** None
**Method:** Tie lichen in an old nylon stocking. Place lichen, wool, and water on to simmer to the desired color.
**Color:** Yellowish Brown 75, deep yBr
**Lightfastness:** L6

**5. Dyestuff:** Lichen (*Stereocaulon* sp.)
**Method:** Tie lichen in an old nylon stocking. Place lichen, wool, and water on to simmer to the desired color.
**Mordant:** None
**Color:** Yellowish Brown 76, light yBr
**Lightfastness:** L2
**Mordant:** Copper
**Color:** Greenish Yellow 104, pale gY
**Lightfastness:** L4–5
**Mordant:** Copper (longer in the dyebath)
**Color:** Greenish Yellow 105, grayish gY
**Lightfastness:** L4–5

# *Mary Lou Wilcox* | California

From a Pomo Indian shaman Mary Lou Wilcox learned a special and profound awareness of plants. Their spirits and their colors belong to

117

Mary Lou's personal experience with the natural world. Her observations of colors passing from plants onto other fibers and the memories of collecting and dyeing are preserved in the yarns she dyes. Mary Lou finds the dye shades are fond reminders of days in the woods and the colors of changing seasons. She collects and experiments with plants from the central region of California where she lives, as well as with those found while traveling or camping, or those she trades with dyers across the country.

Mary Lou's favorite working method is to simmer dyestuff and wool yarns together in the dyebath, and she uses both unmordanted and pre-mordanted yarns as well as the one-pot method (the mordant in the dyebath with the dyestuff and the yarn). She rinses several times after dyeing, including one gentle wash with a mild soap, followed by more rinsing with clean water until the water is clear of soap and excess dye. She reports that there is very little problem with particles getting stuck in the yarn after all her rinsings are completed, although she likes to use more plant material than is usually suggested. Typically, Mary Lou uses a ratio of 3 : 1 (plant-to-wool weight) or even higher, and she feels that this is responsible for bright and fast colors.

*1. Dyestuff:* Elderberries *(Sambucus mexicano),* ripe berries

    *Ratio:* 3–5 pounds freshly picked berries to 1 pound of wool

    *Mordant:* Dissolve approximately 1/4 cup alum, 1/4 cup cream of tartar, and 1/4 cup ammonia (separately from dyebath) in water; have ready to add to dyebath.

    *Method:* Place berries and wool in a large non-reactive pot, and fill with water. Use about 4 gallons per pound of wool. Bring to a simmer and then gently remove yarn. Add dissolved mordants and additives, and stir well into dyebath while maintaining the simmer. Re-enter the yarn; stir gently, and simmer 20–30 minutes. Leave the yarn in the dyebath overnight to cool. Remove yarn, wash gently with a neutral soap, and rinse well before drying out of direct sunlight.

    *Color:* Olive 107, moderate Ol

*Lightfastness:* L4–5

*2. Dyestuff:* Silver dollar eucalyptus *(Eucalyptus polyanthemos),* leaves

These trees and many other Eucalyptus species were introduced to California and Florida as windbreak and

118

field-fencing trees. They are native to Australia, where dyers have also discovered their wonderful color potential.

*Ratio:* At least 3 : 1 leaves to wool; 6 : 1 or 10 : 1 is even better. Use whatever you can fit into your dyepot, or strain out the first lot of leaves after simmering, add more leaves, and simmer longer.

*Method:* Place leaves and wool in a large non-reactive pot and fill with water; use about 4 gallons per pound of dry, clean wool. Bring to a simmer and maintain temperature for at least 1 hour before removing the yarn and adding the mordant. (Some dyers feel that the longer the eucalyptus spends in the pot, the richer the color.) Remove the yarn and add the dissolved mordant while maintaining the temperature of the bath. Put the yarn back into the bath, stirring gently. Simmer for 2 hours or more before cooling the yarn in the bath overnight. Remove, soap wash, rinse, and dry.

*Mordant:* 4 teaspoons chrome, 1 teaspoon tin, and about 1/2 cup cream of tartar, each dissolved separately in water. Add to dyebath after the initial hour of simmering.

*Color:* Reddish Brown 41, deep rBr

*Lightfastness:* L6

*Mordant:* 1 teaspoon tin dissolved in water added to dyebath after the initial hour of simmering

*Color:* Color results are dependent on the length of time the yarn spends in the bath and the time of the year, since eucalyptus produces seasonally dyed colors—often golds in the spring and rusty browns in the autumn. Great variety is possible.

*Color 1:* Reddish Brown 40, strong rBr

*Lightfastness:* L6

*Color 2:* Reddish Orange 36, deep rO

*Lightfastness:* L6

*Color 3:* Orange 48, vivid O

*Lightfastness:* L6

*3. Dyestuff:* Coast redwood or sequoia *(Sequoia sempervirens),* green cones

*Ratio:* 3:1 cones to wool, or higher if possible

*Method:* Place green cones, wool, and about 4 gallons of water in a large non-reactive pot; 4 gallons is sufficient for 1 pound of dry-weight wool. Bring to a simmer and main-

119

tain temperature about 1 hour or until reaching the desired color. Cool yarn in bath overnight. Remove, gently wash with neutral soap, rinse well, dry.

*Mordant:* None
*Color:* Reddish Brown 43, moderate rBr
*Lightfastness:* L3–4

**4. *Dyestuff:*** Madrone (Madrona) *(Arbutus menziesii),* bark
*Ratio:* 3 : 1 bark to wool, or higher if possible
*Method:* Place bark and wool in a large non-reactive pot, and fill with water. Use about 4 gallons per pound of wool. Bring to a simmer and then gently remove yarn. Add dissolved mordants and additives, and stir well into dyebath while maintaining the simmer. Re-enter the yarn; stir gently, and simmer 20–30 minutes. Leave the yarn in the dyebath overnight to cool. Remove yarn and rinse in an ammonia solution of about 1 tablespoon ammonia per 1 quart of water. Wash in a neutral soap bath; rinse well and dry.
*Mordant:* Alum without cream of tartar. Dissolve about 1/4 cup of alum in water; have ready to add to dyebath. Rinse dyed yarn in solution of ammonia and water: 1 tablespoon ammonia per 1 quart of water.
*Color:* Yellowish Brown 75, deep yBr
*Lightfastness:* L5–6

**5. *Dyestuff:*** Mulberries *(Morus* sp.), freshly picked ripe berries
*Ratio:* 3 : 1 fresh ripe berries to dry, clean wool, or higher quantities of berries if possible
*Method:* Place berries with wool in a large non-reactive pot, and fill with water. Use about 4 gallons per pound of wool. Bring to a simmer and then gently remove yarn. Add dissolved mordants and additives, and stir well into dyebath while maintaining the simmer. Re-enter the yarn; stir gently, and simmer 20–30 minutes. Leave the yarn in the dyebath overnight to cool. Remove yarn, wash gently with a neutral soap, and rinse well before drying (out of direct sunlight).
*Mordant:* 1/4 cup alum, 1/4 cup cream of tartar, 1 teaspoon tin, each dissolved separately in water
(Have ready to add to dyebath.)
*Color:* Reddish Purple 243, very dark rP
*Lightfastness:* L5–6 (note: the fastness of this dye is excellent com-

pared to the usual fading of berry dyes, which are perhaps more properly referred to as "stains")

# *Leola Witt-McNie* | Canada

The ritual of dyeing with natural materials is one of Leola Witt-McNie's favorite activities. The days spent collecting dyestuff (with her daughter packed on her back—and accompanied by her dog, goat, and a cat or two) are later brought back to life as she brews the dye, and still later as she chooses from her natural rainbow of dyed yarns for a weaving project.

Leola usually pre-mordants her yarn, but with dyes she knows well, she may mordant during the dyeing. A pre-mordanting process involves the following steps:

1. Dissolve mordant in water sufficient for the amount of wool to be dyed: alum needs 3–4 tablespoons alum and 3–4 gallons of water per pound of wool; chrome needs 3 teaspoons of chrome and 3–4 gallons of water per pound of wool; copper needs 2 tablespoons of copper and 3–4 gallons of water per pound of wool; tin needs 1 teaspoon of tin and 3–4 gallons of water per pound of wool; iron needs 1–2 tablespoons iron and 3–4 gallons of water per pound of wool.
2. Add wool and heat to a simmer; maintain for an hour.
3. Cool yarn in the mordant bath.
4. Remove and rinse thoroughly.

Leola admits to having carefree procedures which are dependent on time and dyestuff availability. She is not concerned with trying to duplicate colors—she prefers surprises from her dyepot.

*1. Dyestuff:* Cherry (*Prunus* sp.), bark
  *Ratio:* 1 pound bark to 1/4 pound clean, dry wool
  *Method:* Chop bark, cover with water, and soak 3 days. Simmer 2–3 hours; let bath cool overnight with bark still in it. Strain out bark. Add pre-mordanted yarn. Simmer yarn in dye for 1 hour; let yarn cool overnight in dyebath. Remove and rinse.
  *Mordant:* Alum
  *Color:* Yellow 90, grayish Y
*Lightfastness:* L3
  *Mordant:* Chrome

*Color:* Olive Brown 95, moderate OlBr
*Lightfastness:* L5
*Mordant:* Copper
*Color:* Yellow 91, dark grayish Y
*Lightfastness:* L3
*Mordant:* Tin
*Color:* Yellow 86, light Y
*Lightfastness:* L3

**2. Dyestuff:** Seaweed (*Gigartina* sp.)
This beautiful burgundy-colored seaweed was collected near Point Holmes, Courtenay, B.C.
*Ratio:* 2 pounds wet, fresh seaweed to 1/4 pound wool
*Method:* Soak seaweed in water to cover for 2 days. Simmer seaweed bath 1 hour and cool. Add pre-mordanted wool and simmer 1 hour. Cool wool in bath overnight. Remove and rinse.
*Mordant:* Alum
*Color:* Yellowish Brown 77, moderate yBr
*Lightfastness:* L2
*Mordant:* Chrome
*Color:* Yellowish Brown 78, dark yBr
*Lightfastness:* L2
*Mordant:* Copper
*Color:* Yellowish Brown 77, moderate yBr
*Lightfastness:* L2
*Mordant:* Tin
*Color:* Yellowish Brown 76, light yBr
*Lightfastness:* L2

**3. Dyestuff:** Horsetail (*Equisetum* sp.)
This rush, a very primitive plant, was gathered at Cowichan Bay, B.C.
*Ratio:* 1 pound fresh horsetails to 1/2 pound wool
*Method:* Soak horsetails overnight in water to cover. Simmer 2 hours and cool with dyestuff in bath. Strain out horsetails and add pre-mordanted yarn. Simmer 1 hour and cool yarn overnight in bath. Remove and rinse.
*Mordant:* Chrome
*Color:* Yellowish Brown 77, moderate yBr
*Lightfastness:* L5
*Mordant:* Copper
*Color:* Greenish Yellow 103, dark gY
*Lightfastness:* L5–6

*Cottonwood
(*Populus *spp.)
leaves and those
from other
related species of
the
family give
excellent fast
and rich dyes.*
(Photo: Jan
Cornies,
courtesy Jones
Sheep Farm)

**4. *Dyestuff:*** Willow *(Salix),* leaves
The leaves used were gathered at Shawnigan Lake, B.C.
**Ratio:** 1 pound leaves to 1/4 pound clean, dry wool
**Method:** Soak leaves overnight in water to cover. Simmer 2–3 hours; cool bath and strain out leaves. Add pre-mordanted wool. Simmer 1 hour and cool yarn in bath. Remove and rinse.
**Mordant:** Alum
**Color:** Yellow 91, dark grayish Y
**Lightfastness:** L3
**Mordant:** Tin
**Color:** Yellow 85, deep Y
**Lightfastness:** L5

**5. *Dyestuff:*** Yew *(Taxus* sp.), wood sawdust
Leola got the sawdust from a friend who had lathe-turned some yew candlesticks.
**Ratio:** 1 pound of sawdust to 1/4 pound clean, dry wool
**Method:** Soak the sawdust overnight in water to cover. Simmer about 3 hours and strain. Add the pre-mordanted wool. Simmer for 45 minutes. Cool the wool overnight in the bath. Remove and rinse.
**Mordant:** Alum
**Color:** Brownish Pink 33, brPk
**Lightfastness:** L2–3

*Mordant:* Chrome
*Color:* Brown 58, moderate Br
*Lightfastness:* L3–4
*Mordant:* Copper
*Color:* Brown 57, light Br
*Lightfastness:* L3–4
*Mordant:* Tin
*Color:* Brown 57, light Br
*Lightfastness:* L2–3

# PART THREE

# SPECIAL DYES AND SPECIAL TECHNIQUES

# Chapter 1.

# Vat Dyes

There are dyers who, for one reason or another, have developed special interests in specific types of dyes, in a group of dyestuffs which produce similar color, in a particular working method, or in an approach to natural dyes to be used for a specific purpose. Other dyers have elected to work primarily with one fiber and adapt a variety of recipes or methods to that fiber. Still other dyers are in business; they use natural dyes on a regular production basis, working on a smaller scale than would an industrial dye house, but dyeing in marketable quantities nonetheless.

## *Fred Gerber* | Florida

The special interest of Fred Gerber lies in bright, clear colors which he sometimes refers to as "spectrum" colors. Because of this, much of his dyeing is done with non-native purchased dyestuffs, although he also uses locally available materials. Within the basic color-range Fred usually works with, he has developed a few favorite dyestuffs—cochineal, indigo, and quercitron—and he has done extensive historical research as well as testing of old recipes in an attempt to duplicate colors and revive interest in the use of natural dyes as a viable color source. Fred's work with indigo is especially noteworthy, and he has figured out some ways to make a sometimes fickle indigo dye really give the range of blues for which it has been so historically important. The following is

127

a distillation of some of Fred's thoughts about indigo as a dyestuff and some methods for using this dye in a home dyeing situation. It is important to remember that natural indigo and synthetic indigo have the very same chemical make-up; the difference between them is the way in which the dyestuff was produced. Natural indigo is derived; synthetic indigo is made by artificially causing the chemical elements to join to form the indigo molecule.

Science tells us that there are over two thousand pigments produced naturally by plants. Of these, fewer than 150 have attained commercial importance. Only a few of this small number have competed successfully with the modern synthetic dyestuffs. Indigo, as a source of permanent blue color, is in this latter group.

It is a mystery how early man discovered the blue of indigo. The glucoside indican, precursor of the color, appears in a wide variety of plants, many of them totally unrelated botanically. It appears in only extremely minute concentrations in each. On exposure to atmospheric oxygen, indican turns blue. But the amounts of indican are normally so small that the color produced from the juices of these plants pressed into cloth is almost imperceptible. It takes. repeated applications of fresh plant juice on the same spot of fabric to produce even a weak indigo blue color.

The plants which have been most important through history for their indigo producing qualities have been the East Indian woody vine *Marsdenia tinctoria,* the oleander *Nerium tinctorium,* woad *(Isatis tinctoria),* some twenty species of the true indigoes (*Indigofera* spp.), as well as the related American indigo, *Baptisia tinctoria,* and the African *Lonchocarpus cyanescens.*

Very early in prehistory man learned to concentrate the indican from these plant juices. There seem to have been only two lines of development aside from the direct dyeing of plant on fiber. One process involved the rotting down or composting of the plants. The quick changes in the glucoside from the water-soluble form to the insoluble blue indigo prevented it from leaching out with other plant juices, and it remained with the reduced fibers of the plants. The compost containing this insoluble pigment was usually made into balls and dried for storage until needed.

The second process for the concentration of indigo was one of extraction, oxidation for conversion to the insoluble form, the precipitation of the indigo, and the drying of the concentrated pigment. The resulting lump indigo has far fewer impurities than that made by the compost method.

These derived products required special treatments to prepare them for application to fibers and fabrics. The indigo had first to be

128

reduced chemically to a colorless compound called indigo white; in this changed state it could be dissolved in any alkaline dyebath. This was called a vat.

As the products from either of these concentration processes had greatly differing pigment contents, no two batches were ever identical. Precise recipes for the use of natural indigo are, therefore, the source of some consternation. Unless one knows the exact amount of indigo in the raw dyestuff, it is impossible to prescribe exact amounts of the two reagents—sodium hydrosulfite and sodium hydroxide, the chemicals most frequently encountered in modern recipes for the necessary indigo reduction and solution. While most modern synthetic indigo may be close to 100 percent pure, the best of the natural indigo sources is only about 48 percent indigo pigment. Most natural indigo sources have much lower than this 48 percent purity.

When dyeing with indigo, the dyer must do two things. First the indigo blue must be changed to indigo white. This is most efficiently done with the modern reducing agent sodium hydrosulfite (sodium dithionite). Second, this indigo white must be dissolved. Any alkali may be used for this second step. Often the reduction and dissolving are done simultaneously by the dyer, but the actual sequence in the dye preparation is always reduction followed by solution.

One problem which arises in many of the modern recipes comes from an imbalance of the reducing agent, the indigo, and the solvent. An exact control of the reducing agent is not as critical as the control of the alkali solvent. It is essential that there be enough of the reducing agent to reduce all of the indigo blue with enough left over to rid the dyebath of any oxygen which may be dissolved in it, as well as any oxygen which may be added to the dyebath during its use. It is necessary too, that there be only enough alkalinity to dissolve the indigo white. In the course of dyeing, any excess of alkalinity will redissolve the indigo which has already been deposited and oxidized on the fibers, and it may be impossible to build up darker colors. It is usually necessary in indigo dyeing to dye repeatedly to build up layers of color in order to obtain more intense colors.

The weaker the alkali is, the slower will be the rate of dissolving of any indigo changed back to indigo white by an excess of sodium hydrosulfite in the bath. If the alkali is too concentrated it may be possible to get dark blue only by making the dyebath as concentrated as will produce the desired intensity in one application. Modern industrial dyeing uses this approach for economic reasons.

A compromise recipe is the substitution of ammonia, a weak alkali, for the usual sodium hydroxide (which is much more powerful) while still retaining the sodium hydrosulfite as the reducing agent. Here is such a compromise recipe:

1. Prepare the indigo stock solution by mixing equal amounts of indigo and sodium hydrosulfite in a small amount of warm water in a glass jar. (A teaspoonful each of indigo powder and sodium hydrosulfite in one cup of water is a good beginning.)

2. After 15 minutes fill the quart jar with household ammonia. Let this stand undisturbed until the liquid is clear and yellow. This may take from one hour to one day, depending on proportions, the actual indigo content, and the temperature. The jar will eventually present a clear yellow solution with a white sludge precipitate at the bottom. The clear yellow part is the indigo stock solution; the sediment is reduced but undissolved indigo.

3. Fill the dyepot with hot tap water to begin the bath. This hot tap water is usually about 140° F (60° C). Add one half teaspoonful of sodium hydrosulfite to the water to get rid of any dissolved oxygen. Let stand 15 minutes.

4. Add part of the indigo stock solution, being careful not to stir in any of the sediment (which would result in a loss of indigo but not provide any dyeing). Stir gently and proceed to dye.

5. When dyeing, steep well-washed wetted wool or any other fiber for 10 minutes in the dyebath. Remove the yarn carefully to avoid excess splashing and the incorporation of air into the bath. Expose the yarn to the air for as long as the steeping period. Re-dye as many times as necessary for the desired intensity of color. Dyeing a small yarn sample will indicate the strength of the dyebath from one dipping given the amount of stock solution added. Longer dyeings will be somewhat darker, as more indigo white will become attached to the yarn. If the yarn turns white again due to an excess of the reducing agent, the alkali should be so weak that it does not redissolve the re-reduced indigo in the time the dyed yarns are being dyed again for a build-up of the indigo.

Another approach to indigo dyeing is possible for those dyers who have natural indigo. This modification of an old method has been adapted to modern circumstances by substituting yeast, sugar, and ammonia for urine. The bacteria of the urine are replaced by the yeast, and the alkali from decomposing amino compounds is supplied by the commercial ammonia. The sugar "feeds" the yeast.

Yeast, in its life processes, requires oxygen for respiration. It has the ability to extract this oxygen from a variety of chemical compounds. If sugar or other foods are supplied, the yeast will thrive, using up the oxygen dissolved in the water. When this oxygen has been exhausted, the yeast will then take oxygen from the water molecules. This leaves free and active hydrogen in the bath. This hydrogen combines with the indigo blue and changes it by modifying its internal bonding to the alkali-soluble indigo white. The addition of ammonia will dissolve this indigo white.

If natural indigo is available to you, you will find the following proportions satisfactory:

> 1 teaspoon powdered natural indigo
> 1 package moist or dry yeast (1 tablespoon)
> 1–3 tablespoons sugar
> 1/2 cup clear non-detergent household ammonia
> 1 gallon warm water suitable for yeast culture (83–104° F; 28–40° C)

Dissolve the sugar in the warm water, and check the temperature so it is not too hot, since this might kill the yeast. Add the yeast. Let stand until the yeast is observed to be active. Meanwhile, add 1/2 cup ammonia to 1 teaspoon indigo in a small container. Stir well to thoroughly wet the indigo. Add the indigo-ammonia mixture to the gallon of yeast-sugar-water solution. Let stand in a warm place until the bath turns yellow. This may take 24 hours or longer as determined by the activity of the yeast and the quantity of indigo in the raw material.

When the dyebath is ready for use, it will be milky yellow with a cloudy sediment of yeast at the bottom and a frothy blue surface. It is imperative that the yeast remain active to reduce the indigo. It may be necessary to add small amounts of sugar from time to time to feed the yeast and encourage its active growth. There seem to be some antiseptic properties in some synthetic indigoes which inhibit yeast growth and this recipe does not work with other than natural indigo.

As a result of the agricultural production of indigo in the American colonial period, there are some residual stands of naturalized *Indigofera suffruticosa* in warmer parts of the southeast and the Mississippi River delta. The dyer who has access to a supply of fresh indigo plants can dye with this plant much in the manner of early man—direct from plant to fiber. Woad *(Isatis tinctoria),* the source of European blue dyes until the Middle Ages, is now a prevalent and noxious weed in many parts of North America. The following procedures can be used successfully with woad as well as the naturalized indigo.

The plants can be gathered when they are in full bloom; before they can dry out, put them to steep or ferment in vats or pots of water.

131

The water-soluble glucoside, indican, leaches from the plants into the water bath. In subtropic summer temperatures this takes between 12 and 18 hours; in more temperate areas, put the pots or jars on the south side of a reflecting building. Tin foil or mirrors can be used to speed heating a bit. It is important to note that the indigo plants have little or no indican in winter or the cooler parts of the year, so it is best to pick them during the summer.

The decoction of plant juices and water constitutes the dyebath. Fibers steeped in this bath will develop a pale pastel blue color after the first airing, and colors will get stronger with successive dippings and airings. The more plant you use for your original steeping, the stronger your dyebath will be; the strength of the dyebath will determine the ultimate color intensity that you can obtain. The blue colors are somewhat clearer and brighter when the dyeing is done outside in the sunshine. And considering the smell of the dyebath—which is not unlike decomposing meat—outside dyeing is desirable. The colors are often grayer when the dyeing is done indoors with the addition of heat from a stove.

In addition to indigo blue colors, the dyer may also obtain colors not generally expected from indigo dyebaths. At temperatures above 140° F (60° C), and especially on soft handspun wool yarns, the indigo dyebath will produce typical blue shades on the outer, looser fibers and pink on the core of more tightly twisted fibers. Further increases in the temperatures tend to produce uniform lavender colors. If the dyebath is strong and the dyeing temperatures are close to the boiling point, a bath from fresh indigo will produce chocolate brown. If the bath is weak, one obtains tan colors. All these colors are substantive in that no mordants are needed or used, and they are of a lasting quality equivalent to indigo blues. They tolerate prolonged exposure to light and repeated washings.

In addition to the naturalized woad and indigo plants, a number of dyers have planted the Japanese *Polygonum tinctorium* in their gardens. It is also possible to obtain the compost preparation of this Japanese indigo plant. Dyeing with any of these fresh plants may also be done directly with the following method:

1. Pack any suitable container with as much foliage as can be jammed in it. Cover with water. Seal the top surface against the air with plastic wrap, squeezing out as many trapped bubbles as possible.

2. Let the mixture stand overnight.

3. After 12 to 18 hours, without splashing or otherwise aerating the dyebath, transfer the bath to a new container to strain out the plant material.

132

4. Steep well-washed wetted fibers in this dyebath for 20 minutes.

5. Remove fibers, without excess splashing, and air for 20 minutes.

6. Repeat the steeping and airing to build up the color.

When a fresh plant-indigo bath has been fully exploited for its blue color, it may be further used for additional colors. By heating the bath above 140° F (60° C), the dyer can obtain the lavender to brown colors previously described. The intensity of color is dependent on the initial strength of the plant decoction. So, while a heated dyebath loses the ability to impart indigo blue, it is still able to provide a variety of other colors from lavender to tan or brown. Indigo-producing plants are able to provide colors other than the "true blue" for which they are traditionally and historically important.

Lightfastness for various shades of indigo blue, tan, and brown varies from L2 to L6 on the testing done. It became apparent that increased fastness to light is provided by either increased steeping time (the time the yarn spends in the indigo dyebath), or an increased number of dippings. More dippings yielded deeper colors that were more fast to light.

The range of the various blue, lavender, and brown colors obtained from the various methods of indigo preparation was extensive and included the following:

Blue: 184, very pale B; 180, very light B; 181, light B; 177, brilliant B; 182, moderate B; 178, strong B; 183, dark B; 179, deep B; 176, vivid B; and 188, blackish B

Lavender: 202, very pale pB; and 203, pale pB (pB is the Centroid designation for Purplish Blue)

Tan: 33, brPk (Brownish Pink)

Brown: 58, moderate Br; and 61, grayish Br

# *Junko Sato Pollack* | New York

Another dyer concerned with successive dipping methods is Junko Sato Pollack. For many generations her father's family were indigo dyers, and in her mother's family there were many doctors who used herbal medicines. Junko's interests reflect her Japanese heritage, as she is involved in studies and work using traditional Japanese (and Chinese) herbal medicines, and dyes that tie in closely with ancient Japanese folk beliefs. Junko is a dyer in the traditional Japanese fashion, and she also weaves traditional fabric using ikat and other dye techniques.

133

Junko shares here some of her knowledge of natural dyeing and folk beliefs in Japan, and methods of using two traditional dyes: purple root and safflower.

In ancient Japan the art of dyeing originated from a religious ritual of purification intended to borrow the protective powers of nature: trees, fire, water, and so on. After bast fiber fabrics were woven, before they were made into garments, they were purified by washing in wood ash (the result of burning trees), and by soaking in mud or in a mineral hot spring. In such processes of scouring, bleaching, and mordanting, the tannin in the bast fiber reacts with iron and other minerals to modify its original color. This actually strengthens and softens the bast fiber and improves its appearance. The resulting change of quality and strength of the fabric by means of a purification process was an indication to the ancient Japanese that the nature gods had provided some sort of protection.

Dye plants were used by rulers as a means of displaying their powers, by transferring the powers of the nature gods to themselves through the plants. From ancient Chinese philosophy Japan inherited an elaborate system of metaphysical speculation in which colors played a key role. The ancient concept of power manifestation through natural dyes is still reflected in the rituals of the royal court and shrines in Japan today. The costumes and ornaments are dyed in the same manner as they were in ancient times, and each color symbolizes court rank in the descending order of purple, red, green, and blue. In the tea ceremony, developed at a relatively late date in Japan's history, purple napkins are used by men and red by women, one extension of this practice of ranking colors hierarchically.

There was little distinction made between the dyeing and medicinal uses of plants. Since most plants used for dyeing also possessed medicinal properties, concoctions made from them were used internally as well as externally. Folk beliefs in the medicinal uses of dyes remain alive in modern Japanese daily life. For example, fabrics dyed with purple root, or *Lithospermum,* are used as undergarments for the prevention of stomach trouble and skin diseases, as well as for protection against other causes of disease. Bedding *(futon)* made with purple-dyed fabric is also believed to prevent colds. While at first glance naive-seeming, such beliefs are not entirely unfounded in fact. The dye produced from *Lithospermum* root is volatile and has been found to contain an active antibacterial agent. This root is also used in herbal medicine as a sedative, an antidote for poisons, a contraceptive, and to cure hemorrhoids, smallpox, skin diseases, cuts, and burns.

In another example, safflower *(Carthamus tinctorius)* has widespread uses in folk medicine. One extant folk tradition calls for the use of red dye from safflower or madder to dye a corner of indigo-dyed cotton bath towels for newborn babies. The red section of the towel is used only for wiping the baby's face, a procedure once thought to grant protection from smallpox. In this case, the red dye from the plant, believed to help blood circulation and to stimulate tissue regeneration, is associated with the color that symbolizes the protection of the sun god. Safflower red is also used for women's undergarments; the plant is said to have medicinal properties against such conditions as amenorrhea and prolonged postpartum discharge.

There are also many folk beliefs concerning indigo dye. Indigo was originally considered a royal color because it was extremely difficult to manufacture. As the techniques of making and maintaining indigo dye became increasingly sophisticated, however, the use of this dye was popularized and its use was no longer limited to royalty. It finally came to be used by peasants for their hemp and cotton work garments. There is a surviving folk belief that the strong smell of the dye keeps away poisonous snakes and scorpions; it is also thought to counteract poisons. Attempts are being made to investigate these beliefs for scientific validity. In any case, it is certain that natural indigo dye strengthens cotton and hemp fabrics when they are dyed a natural dark indigo blue.

The dyes Junko produced using the following methods for purple root and safflower are beautiful. The resultant colors are very clear and bright, and have a subtlety beyond that of most natural dyes. While the dyes did fade under the extremely bright light of the weatherometer, this should not preclude their use for articles which would not be subjected to such high exposures to light. The articles could certainly be re-dyed if need be, and this is one way in which many traditional textiles (particularly those of India) were dyed. If the color faded, the articles were simply dyed again. The colors from purple root and safflower dyes done in the traditional Japanese manner here in the United States are worth the effort.

*1. Dyestuff:* Purple root (*Lithospermum erythroryzon* Sieb et Zucc. —soft purple root, or *Lithospermum euchroma Royle Arnebia euchroma*—hard purple root)
*Lithospermum* plants are perennials which grow wild in overgrown fields or slopes of miscanthus and other wild grasses. They bear white flowers during summer, and after flowering the plants develop gray, rock-hard seeds. Hence the name *Lithos* (stone)-*spermum* (seed). The roots are dug out between July and October, dried, and used as medicine or as dye. Interestingly enough, various groups of Native Americans have used the roots of *Lithospermum* species to produce red and yellow dyes, as well as for birth-control medicine.

135

**Preparation of the Fiber:** Wood ash is used as a mordant as well as a fixative for the dye. Camellia tree *(Camellia japonica)*, sweetleaf *(Symplocos chinensis* var. Druce), sapphire berry or Asiatic sweetleaf *(Symplocos paniculata* Mig), aniseed tree *(Illicium religiosum* Sieb et Zucc.) and *Eurya japonica* are used for their high content of alum in the ash. An alum mordant can be used in combination with the wood ash or without the wood ash.

**Mordant:** Wood ash and soybean juice

*Ash Solution:* Burn any of the trees listed above and take the ash. Boil 1 1/2 gallons of water in a pot, add 1 quart wood ash, and return to boil for 10 minutes. Turn off the heat. Let the solution stand until the ash sediment settles at the bottom. Drain only the clear top solution. The color of the solution should be bright golden, and it should feel squeaky when rubbed between fingers. If it feels slimy, it is too strong. Dilute with water until squeaky. For 1 pound of fiber use 1 1/2 gallons of ash solution.

*Soybean juice (gojiru):* Soak 1 cup soybeans in enough water to cover. When the beans are swollen and soft, crush or grind them and soak in 1 1/2 gallons of water. Strain and reserve the liquid; it should look like watered-down milk. The ground soybeans can be dried and re-used.

**Mordanting the Fiber:** 1. Soak the fiber in freshly made ash solution. Squeeze and dry completely. Repeat this three times.

2. Soak the fiber in the soybean solution. Squeeze and dry completely.

3. Repeat steps 1 and 2 over a period of three or four days, ending finally after step 1. The same solution is used for the entire process.

4. Store the dried fiber in a drawer or any dark place for two months (or at least two weeks) for oxidation. The longer the storage period, the better the results will be.

**Extracting the Dye and Dyeing:** 1. Boil a large quantity of water in a large pot.

2. Put purple roots in a mortar and pour boiling water on them to cover.

3. Work out the dye by grinding and breaking the roots with a pestle in a mortar (this takes 10–20 minutes).

4. Strain the dye solution into the dyepot through a linen or cotton bag. Repeat until enough dye solution to cover the fiber is collected.

5. Heat the solution to 140–158° F (60–70° C) and soak the fiber in the dye. Do not boil the dye solution, as the purple color will be lost.

6. Repeat steps 1 through 5 as long as the roots give out dye and the desired color is obtained.

7. Rinse in cold water and dry.

*Color:* With alum mordant and 4 repeats on wool—Purple 223, moderate P

*Lightfastness:* L2–3

*Color:* With alum mordant and 8 repeats on wool—Purple 224, dark P

*Lightfastness:* L3–4

*Color:* 4 repeats on cotton/hemp fabric—Purple 223, moderate P

*Lightfastness:* Cotton threads less than L2; hemp L5–6

*Color:* 4 repeats on silk fabric—Purple 223, moderate P

*Lightfastness:* Less than L2

*2. Dyestuff:* Safflower *(Carthamus tinctorius),* petals

Flowers should be picked in the early morning in July and August; pick only the top two-thirds of the petals, as the remaining part of the petals will continue to grow and can be picked again the next morning. The picked petals can be dried or made into safflower cakes for storage. If you want to grow safflowers in your garden, plant the seeds in April after the last frost.

*Preparation of Safflower Cakes:* Rinse out dust, oil, and yellow juice from the freshly picked petals in cold running water. Spread washed petals evenly over a straw mat about 1 inch thick, and cover with another straw mat. Sprinkle water over the mats 3 times a day. Keep the petals moist and in the sun. Leave the flower petals to ferment for 2–3 days. As fermentation begins, the yellowish petals turn bright red; when separated, they are stringy. Mash the fermented flower petals with a mortar and pestle. Form into flat cakes about 1" in diameter. Spread cakes over straw mats and dry in the sun until they dry completely; this will take about 2–3 days in sunny conditions. Cakes should be taken indoors at night. If moisture remains in the cakes, it will disturb the color while in storage. These dry cakes can be stored indefinitely.

137

**Ratio:** For 1 pound of cotton, silk, hemp, or flax (wool is not suitable) use 1 pound of safflower (cakes or dried petals); 1 1/3 ounces (8% of fiber weight) potassium carbonate for #1 Bath; 3/5 ounce (4% of fiber weight) potassium carbonate for #2 Bath; 1 3/5 ounce (10% of fiber weight) citric acid; and enough of a 2% solution of acetic acid to cover the fiber.

**Method I:** 1. Put safflower cakes or dried safflower petals in a cotton bag and soak in warm water overnight. After soaking, squeeze out yellow dye. The yellow dye can be used for dyeing yellow (see Method II).

2. Rinse the bag of squeezed flower petals in running water. Wash out until the water runs clear or until most of the yellow dye is removed.

3. Dissolve the 1 1/3 ounces potassium carbonate in water measuring 30 times the dry weight of the fiber, about 4 gallons.

4. Soak squeezed safflower petals in the first potassium carbonate solution (#1 bath) for 3 hours or until all the dye seeps out of the petals and they become translucent brown. The dye solution should be reddish brown. Drain the petals. If the petals still have red in them, repeat the soaking in the second solution (4%) of potassium carbonate (#2 bath).

5. Slowly pour the citric acid into the dye solution, stirring gently. When the dye solution is neutralized, white bubbles appear and the color of the dye solution turns to red or pink (depending on the dye content of the safflower).

6. Pre-soak the fiber for 30 minutes; then place it in the dye solution. Remove and squeeze out the excess liquid. Hang up to dry to allow the fiber to oxidize.

7. While the fiber is drying, heat the same dye solution up to 140° F (60° C). Do not boil. The second dye solution can be added to the dyebath. If a cold dyebath is necessary, continue the process without heating the dyebath. Add the fiber; turn off the heat, and let it cool.

8. Repeat this process until the desired shade is obtained.

9. After dyeing, soak fiber in 2% acetic acid solution

(you can dilute white vinegar 1:1 with water and get about a 2% acidic solution). Keep fiber in the solution about 30 minutes, and then rinse in cold water. This solution fixes the dye.

10. When the red dye is all taken up, the dye solution will look slightly yellow. If there is any red dye left in the dye solution, heat it to 140° F (60° C) and soak a swatch of cotton to take up all the remaining dye. Rinse, dry, and save the swatch for future use. The dye in the swatch can be extracted in the next potassium carbonate solution (step 4). (To repeat step 4 with the swatch, first soak the swatch until it becomes white, then proceed by adding squeezed safflower petals.)

*Note:* Any oiliness disturbs the dye penetration, so all fiber must be well scoured. When handling the fiber, use rubber gloves or glass rods and avoid contacting fiber with hands. Even a small amount of body oil can disturb the dye absorption/adsorption.

*Method II:* To obtain yellow from safflower, use the following ratio of dye and mordants/additives to dry weight of fiber. This color will work for wool in addition to the fibers which can be dyed using Method #I.

*Ratio:* Yellow dye obtained from Method #I—20 times the dry weight of the fiber
Acetic acid/citric acid—2% of the weight of the dry safflowers
Tin—2% of the dry weight of the fiber
Water—20 times the dry weight of the fiber

*Procedure:* Heat the yellow dye solution to about 175° F (80° C), or until the first bubble rises, just before the boiling point. Add citric acid to the solution and stir well. Put pre-soaked and squeezed fiber in the dye solution. Gently boil for 20–30 minutes. Turn off heat and let the dye solution cool with the fiber. Soak overnight or until it is cool. Heat the mordant to dissolve the tin. Add the fiber to the mordant solution for 20 minutes. Return the fiber to the dye solution when it has been heated up to about 175° F (80° C). Gently simmer for 30 minutes. Let it cool in the bath, drain, rinse, and dry.

*Color:* Bath 1 and 2 on cotton/hemp fabric—Purplish Red 255, strong pR

*Lightfastness:* Cotton threads less than L2; hemp L5–6

*Color:* Tin mordant on wool yarn—Yellow 84, strong Y

*Lightfastness:* L2–3

*Color:* Tin mordant on silk fabric—Yellow 85, deep Y

*Lightfastness:* L2–3

*Color:* Baths #1 and #2 on silk fabric—Reddish Orange 35, strong rO

*Lightfastness:* L2

# Chapter 2.

# Putrefaction and Solar Dyes

Two other dyers who are involved in the closely related semi-vat, putrefaction, fermentation, and solar dyeing methods are Christine LeMar and Marilyn Lorance. Their methods vary somewhat, but they are working in the same direction—to get color from plants onto fiber without cooking on a stove.

## *Christine LeMar* | Wisconsin

Christine uses a lot of big plastic buckets, tubs, pots, and pails plus an assortment of other containers in her outdoor dye area. She soaks her yarns in mordant; she does not simmer them on the stove. She uses both soaking and simmering baths for the actual dyeing. Christine uses her own handspun yarns, and she especially enjoys being able to capture the beauty of natural living things by dyeing with them in the summer, thus preserving the color to brighten drab winter days. Her methods are simple and untimed; she works almost instinctively.

Here are the formulas for Christine's mordants. Each is mixed in water in a 3- to 4-gallon plastic pail. About a pound of clean wool is then entered, and a lid is snapped onto the pail. The yarn remains in the mordant bath for at least a day, until it is ready to be dyed. Sometimes Christine makes double-strength mordant baths by doubling the amount of mordant per pound of fiber.

141

Mordant 1:  2–4 tablespoons alum plus 2–4 tablespoons of cream of tartar

Mordant 2:  2–3 teaspoons chrome; sometimes a cup of vinegar is added

Mordant 3:  1 heaping tablespoon tin plus 1 tablespoon oxalic acid crystals or 10 drops nitric acid

Mordant 4:  2 tablespoons iron crystals plus 1 tablespoon oxalic acid crystals

Mordant 5:  2 or more tablespoons copper (use enough to turn the water very blue) plus 1 tablespoon urea crystals

Mordant 6:  1 cup vinegar plus 2 tablespoons cream of tartar plus 1/4 cup baking soda: add these to the bath and when it begins to bubble, add 2 tablespoons of alum and stir; add the yarn while it's still fizzing

Christine's methods for dyeing a skein of yarn are close to many of those discussed in the preceding section (Part Two). In addition to one-color skeins, she also dyes coordinated color skeins in which the color changes throughout the skein. Sometimes these yarns are called space-dyed, meaning that part of the space on the length of yarn is one color, another section is a second color, etc. Here are six methods Christine uses to intentionally vary the color on a skein of yarn:

1. Soak the yarn in one double-strength mordant for 7–10 days. Rinse the yarn and hang it until it stops dripping. Suspend the skein by a rope from a pulley over the dyepot, with the whole skein submerged in the pot. Turn on the heat, and when steam first starts to rise from the pot, gradually lift the skein from the pot over a 15–30 minute period until only the bottom 1/4 skein remains in the dye by the time it starts to boil. Then turn off the heat, and leave the bottom 1/4 of the skein in the pot with the bath to cool overnight. Remove the skein and hang for a week before rinsing. After the week of oxidation, rinse the skein and put on a blocker to dry. If it dries pale or the color is unsuitable, re-dye it, either in the same bath or a different one.

2. Apply multiple mordants to the skein before dyeing, beginning with alum and working toward mordants that have more coloring effects on the yarn. Prepare double-strength mordant baths, and put 1/3 to 1/2 of the wetted skein in the mordant bath with the end of the skein not in the bath but suspended above the pail or tied to the side so it does not fall in. The mordant should be stirred every day; take the skein out to oxidize briefly while you stir the mordant. Take about a week to soak the first end of the skein. Then, place the other end of the skein in a second mordant bath and repeat the process. If you want to

mordant the middle section of the skein separately from the ends, you can tie the ends together, and just soak the folded middle portion of the skein. You can also overlap the sections which have various mordants (for example, copper over alum and chrome).

3. Mordant the whole skein in either tin or alum. Dye the whole skein in one dyebath. To vary the color along the skein, dip a portion of the dyed skein into a second mordant bath and leave until the color changes, or add a second mordant quantity to the dyebath after removing the whole skein of yarn. Dissolve the second mordant in the dyebath, and re-enter just a portion of the already dyed skein.

4. Use any of these mordanting methods above with two other dyebaths. This gives you a good change of color, and it is a neat trick for using up tail ends of dyebaths, or if you have only a small portion of dye.

5. Mordant the skein of yarn. Using some dyestuff you know to be reliable, wrap up the wet skein of yarn inside a layer of plant material. Put the package (you can tie the plant material around the yarn or roll it in a cheesecloth piece) over steam; it can be suspended with the same rope and pulley system used for Method I above. You can also put the tied bundle directly into water and simmer until dyed.

6. This method is called cross dyeing and is used in the dye industry for creating some heather yarns or yarns with blended tonal qualities. Before dyeing, blend two fibers together during the carding process, and then spin the yarn. The yarn is then dyed by any method, and the resultant color will be variable depending on how the fibers take the dye. The fibers can also be pre-mordanted before carding, so wool mordanted with two (or more) mordants will be spun and dyed to give a multi-toned yarn. If you are not a handspinner, it is possible to dye yarns made from two different fibers in the same dyebath, and use the yarns together, as if they were one, for knitting, crocheting, or any other fiber project. Fabrics of two or more fibers can be dyed with one mordant and result in a variably toned color.

Some examples of Christine's coordinated skeins' colors are these:

*1. Dyestuff:* Logwood (*Haematoxylon campechianum*)
   *Mordant:* Tin and alum
      *Color:* Light end of skein—Reddish Purple 245, grayish rP
              Dark end of skein—Reddish Purple 242, dark rP
*Lightfastness:* L4–5
   *Mordant:* Copper
      *Color:* Light end of skein—Neutral 265, medium gray
              Dark end of skein—Neutral 266, dark gray

*Lightfastness:* L4–5
   *Mordant:* Alum and copper
     *Color:* Light end of skein—Violet 211, moderate V
       Dark end of skein—Neutral 267, black
*Lightfastness:* L4–5

  **2. *Dyestuff:*** Brazilwood (*Caesalpinia* sp.)
   *Mordant:* Chrome
     *Color:* Light end of skein—Purplish Pink 253, grayish pPk
       Dark end of skein—Purple 218, strong P
*Lightfastness:* L4–5
   *Mordant:* Chrome and copper
     *Color:* Light end of skein—Purplish Pink 253, grayish pPk
       Dark end of skein—Reddish Purple 242, dark rP
*Lightfastness:* L4–5
   *Mordant:* Alum, tin, and chrome
     *Color:* Light end of skein—Purplish Red 255, strong pR
       Dark end of skein—Purplish Red 257, very deep pR
*Lightfastness:* L4–5

# Marilyn Lorance | Arizona

Marilyn dyes in simmering water baths, but she also dyes her finely handspun wools in the sun. She sometimes uses pre-mordanted yarn, and sometimes puts the mordants into the dyebath. Marilyn may simmer the dyestuff in a water bath and then let it sit in the sun for a while before adding the yarn. Or, she may simmer the dyestuff in the bath, strain out the dyestuff, then add the yarn and let it sit in the sun. Marilyn may also put the dyestuff in one of her gallon glass jars and let it sit for a while covered with water, and then either strain or not strain out the dyestuff before adding the yarn. Her working methods are flexible and fun, and the results are beautiful colors on a yarn with a lovely, gentle feel. Marilyn's methods are simple and can be adopted by any dyer with access to the sun.

  **1. *Dyestuff:*** Cochineal, handpicked in Arizona *(Dactylopius* sp.)
         The commercially available species is *Dactylopius coccus*, but other species of *Dactylopius* are found elsewhere in North America and also produce dye.
    *Ratio:* One ounce of cochineal will easily dye 1 pound of wool.
  *Method:* Simmer cochineal and mordant in water until distinct color has leached out of the bugs; this may take 30–60

minutes. Strain out bugs (if desired) and add yarn. Pour the dyebath and yarn into a glass container and place in the sun until you like the color of the yarn. Remove and rinse.

*Mordant:* Alum (4 tablespoons for 1 pound wool)
*Color:* Purplish Pink 247, strong pPk
*Lightfastness:* L4–5
*Mordant:* Tin (1–2 teaspoons for 1 pound wool)
*Color:* Purplish Pink 250, moderate pPk
*Lightfastness:* L4–5

**2. *Dyestuff:*** Eucalyptus (*Eucalyptus* sp.), leaves
*Ratio:* 1-gallon jar full of leaves and covered with water to about 4 ounces of wool
*Method:* Place leaves in gallon glass jar and cover with water. Line lid with plastic or waxed paper and screw it on the jar. Let the jar sit in the sun for several weeks. Strain out the leaves. Add pre-mordanted yarn. Let the yarn sit in the bath in the sun for 13 days. Remove and rinse.
*Mordant:* Copper (3 tablespoons for 1 pound of wool)
*Color:* Greenish Yellow 105, grayish gY
*Lightfastness:* L3

**3. *Dyestuff:*** Logwood *(Haematoxylon campechianum)*
*Ratio:* 1/2 pound of wood chips will easily dye 1 pound of wool
*Method:* Fill a gallon glass jar with logwood chips. Fill the jar with water. Add wetted pre-mordanted yarn; put on the lid. Let the jar sit in the sun until the desired color is obtained. Remove and rinse the yarn.
*Mordant:* Alum
*Color:* Reddish Purple 245, grayish rP
*Lightfastness:* L2

**4. *Dyestuff:*** Madder *(Rubia tinctorum)* and brazilwood *(Caesalpinia* sp.)
*Ratio:* 1/2 pound of madder and 1/2 pound of brazilwood will dye 1 pound of wool.
*Method:* Prepare dyebath by simmering the madder and brazilwood in water to cover for 1 hour. Strain out dyestuff. Pour bath into glass jars. Add pre-mordanted yarn and put on the lid. Let sit in the sun until the desired color is reached. Remove and rinse.
*Mordant:* Tin

    *Color:* Red 16, dark R
*Lightfastness:* L5–6
  *Mordant:* Tin in madder bath first, then in brazilwood exhaust
      bath
   *Color:* Yellowish Pink 26, strong yPk
*Lightfastness:* L4–5

*Note:* With very strong dyebaths, it is possible to easily top-dye or over-dye by simply removing the yarn from one jar to another—as from a madder bath in one jar to a brazilwood bath in a second jar. You will need to rinse between baths to prevent bleeding of baths, unless you don't mind that variable.

# Chapter 3.

# Production Dyes
# for Silk and Wool

Cheryl Kolander and Linda Berry Walker live at opposite ends of the continent, yet they have a great deal in common. Both women are professional dyers involved in commercial production. But more than that expertise is shared, for each deeply appreciates nature, the dyes that can be obtained from natural materials, and the fibers she is dyeing. They are convinced that natural dyes impart a special beauty and richness that synthesized dyes can neither duplicate nor match. In an era of machines and mass markets their hand-dyed products are very special.

## *Cheryl Kolander* | Oregon

Dyer Cheryl Kolander loves silk, loves color, and loves to put color onto silk. She is one of very few people in the world who dye silk threads with natural dyes for commercial trade. Her colors are soft and subtle, yet rich and alive. The rainbow comes to life when she pulls skeins of lustrous silk from her pots. Cheryl's products emulate ancient Oriental silks found in robes that were worn by the upper classes. Yet they are absolutely appropriate for contemporary textiles. Cheryl's work reflects her appreciation and understanding of the color and beauty in the natural world.

In order to get the widest color range possible from her dyestuff, Cheryl utilizes mordants in varying amounts before, in, and after the

147

dyeing. She also uses acids to alter colors (alkalis can injure silk), and varied lengths of time in the dyebath. The following outline of her cochineal dyeing method indicates how the range of color is obtained. Her working method for scouring and handling silk is similar to that discussed in Chapter 4 (of Part One).

*Dyestuff:* Cochineal *(Dactylopius coccus),* dried insects

*Mordant:* Mordants: For each pound of silk use 4–4 1/2 gallons of water and the following amounts of mordants—

Alum: 3–4 ounces alum plus 1 ounce cream of tartar
Chrome: 1/6 ounce
Iron: 1/6–1/2 ounce
Tin: 1/2–2 ounces plus 1 ounce cream of tartar

*Note:* Alum and tin are usually used to pre-mordant the yarn. Iron and chrome are often used as afterbaths and are dissolved in cold water. The dyed and cooled silk is entered into this cold mordant bath and removed after the desired color-change occurs.

*Dyebaths:* The baths are more or less standard simmering water baths as outlined in earlier chapters. Depending on the color range sought, the following amounts of cochineal are used per pound of silk—

Rose, medium rose, light rose: 4 ounces cochineal with tin pre-mordant and chrome afterbath

Crimson, pure red: 8 ounces cochineal with tin pre-mordant and chrome afterbath

Coppery plum, light plum, lavender rose: 3 ounces cochineal with tin pre-mordant and iron afterbath

Violet, medium violet, light violet: 3 ounces cochineal with alum pre-mordant and iron afterbath

Lavender, pale lavender: 1 ounce (or more) cochineal with chrome mordant (an exhaust dye using wool can be used for lavender)

*Note:* Cheryl also adds acid (vinegar will work) to these baths; this tends to orange the dye. Soap rinses tend to blue the colors.

The range of colors Cheryl obtains from cochineal falls within the Centroid Color groups Reddish Purple, Purplish Pink, and Purplish

Red. It appears that nearly every color included in those groups is possible to attain by means of varied mordants, acids, soap, and ratio of cochineal to silk. Some of the colors obtained were Purplish Red 262, grayish pR; Purplish Pink 247, strong pPk; Reddish Purple 237, strong rP; Purplish Pink 251, dark pPk; Purplish Pink 253, grayish pPk; and Neutral 264, light gray.

Lightfastness seems to be very good, and of the eleven samples tested in the weatherometer, one ranked L3, one ranked L4, and the others were L5 and L5–6. The fading in most cases appeared to be more a factor of loss of luster than of loss of color depth, however. Many fibers (including silk) deteriorate in direct sunlight, and the deterioration of the fiber itself may have been a point to consider with the silk lightfastness testing.

# *Linda Berry Walker* | New Jersey

At the other end of the continent from Cheryl is Linda Berry Walker, who raises the largest flock of purebred Romney sheep on the east coast. She markets white, natural gray, and brown-colored commercially spun and handspun wool in addition to her own naturally dyed mohair and wool. Linda's range of colors covers the spectrum and embodies her love for the materials and the processes of dyeing with nature. Her idea of a good time is a walk through the woods to gather dyestuffs and then chopping, cooking, and simmering them on a wood fire and dyeing a lot of wool. She tends to avoid imported dyestuffs unless used in combination with local flora. Linda is one of those fortunate people who have been able to combine a career with the life they love.

*Linda Berry Walker uses a stick to stir cooking plants. Note the "stove" made from a barrel. A wood fire is built below; the smoke escapes through vents on one side at the top.*

149

Linda admits to not favoring the use of recipes; she depends on intuition and tends to put in lumps or handfuls rather than calculate ratios and weights. She finds that her colors are reflective of her environment, with colors and available dyestuff varying from wet to dry years and with the seasonal changes. Her environment and her methods have paid off, for her yarns are loved and purchased by leading New York textile design studios as well as craft-fair goers.

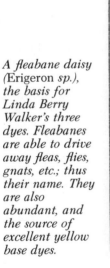

*A fleabane daisy (Erigeron sp.), the basis for Linda Berry Walker's three dyes. Fleabanes are able to drive away fleas, flies, gnats, etc.; thus their name. They are also abundant, and the source of excellent yellow base dyes.*

Here are three of Linda's favorite colors using alum–pre-mordanted yarn, both wool and the lustrous mohair:

150

*1. Dyestuff:* Fleabane daisy (*Erigeron* sp.), all above-ground parts
*Ratio:* 4-gallon pot full of freshly cut daisy plants to 1 pound of wool
*Mordant:* Alum pre-mordant
*Method:* Fill the pot with plants and cover with water. Simmer on a wood fire until all the plant matter is completely limp and wilted. Strain out the dyestuff. Add 1 pound well-wetted pre-mordanted wool. Simmer 30 minutes. Remove yarn and add 2–3 tablespoons iron, depending on the depth of green desired. Stir well and re-immerse the yarn. Simmer 30 minutes more. Let the dyebath cool until the yarn can be handled. Rinse well using soap. Rinse well using clear water.
*Color:* Yellow Green 122, grayish YG
*Lightfastness:* L6

*2. Dyestuff:* Fleabane daisy (*Erigeron* sp.) and cochineal *(Dactylopius coccus)*
*Ratio:* A 4-gallon pot full of freshly cut daisy herbaceous parts plus 1 ounce of ground cochineal to 1 pound of wool
*Mordant:* Alum pre-mordant
*Method:* Fill the pot with plants and cover with water. Simmer on a wood fire until all the plant matter is completely limp and wilted. Strain out the dyestuff. Add 1 pound well-wetted alum–pre-mordanted wool. Simmer 60 minutes. Remove yarn. Boil 1 ounce of cochineal in 2 quarts water for 10 minutes. Strain out any insects as you pour the cochineal liquor into the fleabane daisy bath. Stir the two dyes together and re-immerse the yarn. Simmer 30–60 minutes to the desired shade. Let the yarn cool in the dyebath until it can be handled. Rinse with soap. Rinse with clear water.
*Color:* Reddish Orange 39, grayish rO
*Lightfastness:* L5–6

*3. Dyestuff:* Fleabane daisy (*Erigeron* sp.) and indigo
*Ratio:* A 4-gallon pot full of freshly cut daisies (all above-ground parts) and several squirts of indigo–sulfuric acid mixture to 1 pound of wool
*Mordant:* Alum pre-mordant

*Method:* Fill the pot with plants and cover with water. Simmer on a wood fire until all the plant matter is completely limp and wilted. Strain out dyestuff. Add 1 pound well-wetted alum–pre-mordanted wool. Simmer 60 minutes. Have ready another dyepot (same size and same temperature) to which several squirts of concentrated indigo–sulfuric acid mixture have been added. Stir well to mix the indigo. (Your indigo–sulfuric acid mixture can be prepared by gradually mixing 1 ounce of indigo powder into 5 ounces of sulfuric acid.) Keep the mixture at a constant temperature of about 100° F (37.8° C) for 8–12 hours. Stir occasionally. In a couple of days stir in 2–3 teaspoons of powdered chalk. Store in a tightly capped container, preferably glass. Remove the yarn from the daisy bath into the heated indigo bath. Simmer for 60 minutes; cool overnight in the bath. Rinse with soap followed by rinsing in clear water.

*Color:* Bluish Green 160, strong bG

*Lightfastness:* L5–6

# Chapter 4.
# Dyeing Natural Basketry Materials

## Alice Wansor | New York

Another dye method deserving attention is that of dyeing natural fibers other than the usual ones like wool, silk, cotton, and linen. New York resident Alice Wansor dyes the splints, barks, reeds, and vines she uses in her basketry. Dyeing basketry materials with natural dyes has long been practiced by native peoples across North America, but the earlier native dyes depended primarily upon such things as black walnut hulls, bloodroot, rabbitbrush, and ochres to provide the color. Alice has taken the techniques one step further and experimented with many dyes and methods to get the effects she wants.

She has learned a few tricks like putting new reed baskets into strong (actually undrinkable) coffee or tea and leaving the baskets in it overnight. Presto! An antique-looking basket. Or she sometimes dips just part of a completed basket into a dyebath to dye only a portion of it.

Alice makes her baskets "from scratch," just as native Americans did until recently, when prepared materials became commercially available. She harvests materials near a family cabin in the Maine woods as well as closer to home. She feels that natural dyes impart softer and more desirable colors to her baskets than do synthetic dyes, and that as natural colors fade, they still retain a certain richness.

Alice offers these hints for materials to use for baskets that can be dyed with natural dyes. The amount of material dyed per bath is vari-

*A selection of natural basket fibers are here being dyed by Alice Wansor.*

able, Alice notes, since you can use the bath over and over until it is exhausted, and lightly dyed materials can be top-dyed for darker colors. The basketry materials discussed below are those found in Alice's area; you will probably be able to find the same or related plants in your area. Experimentation is fun and educational. In general, the materials should be dried after harvesting, and then re-wetted by soaking in warm water prior to their usage.

1. *Honeysuckle vine or ivy vine:* Cut long runners and pull off the leaves. Coil in bundles and then boil for 3 hours. Rub off the bark and cut off knots with a sharp pen knife. Before using, soak the vines for 30 minutes or more in warm water.

2. *Cattail leaves:* Cut in the fall, preferably in September and October. Cut off the heavy (bottom) end. Thread the leaves on a string, and hang to dry. Before using soak 30 minutes to an hour in water; then wrap in a wet towel until used.

3. *Dried field grasses:* These are best used in bunches for core material when coiling or twining into a stable basket of reed or vine. Broomsbeard *(Andropogon Virginicus)* and other tall, smooth-stemmed prairie grasses are good.

4. *Barks:* Bark should not be removed from living trees as it will kill the tree or at the very least make it susceptible to disease. Cut the bark from freshly cut trees in the spring or summer when the sap is up. Use smooth bark from young trees right away in splint work. Older bark must be soaked in water to make it pliable. Some good barks to use are from these trees: Birch *(Betula* sp.); basswood or American linden *(Tilia*

154

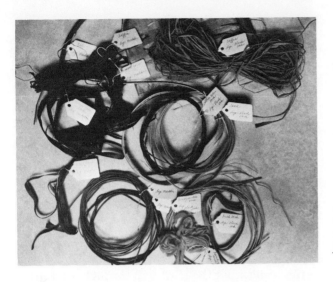

*A selection of naturally dyed natural fibers from Alice Wansor's dyepot.*

*Surrounded by samples of her natural baskets, Alice Wansor adds the finishing touches to a small plaited or woven basket.*

sp.); white cedar (*Thuja occidentalis*); the bark of the western red cedar (*Thuja plicata*) is also good to use, and was worked extensively by Northwest Coastal Indians; in the latter two cases, use the inner bark for best results; white pine inner bark *(Pinus strobus)*; hemlock inner bark (*Tsuga* sp.); and black oak bark (*Quercus* sp.).

5. *Corn* (Zea) *husks:* Separate inner leaves near the ear. Spread on newspaper to dry. Use the leaves as core material in coiling or twining

into a more stable basket of reed or vines. The Nez Perce Indians made extensive use of corn husks in bags using Indian hemp *(Apocynum cannabinum)* twined as the warp threads; the corn husks were dyed with natural materials in many cases and later supplemented with commercially made and dyed trade yarns.

When Alice dyes her basketry materials she follows these simple and practical rules:

Add the mordant to the dyebath with the basketry material. Do not pre-mordant. (This way the basket materials are not boiled too much.)

Boil as little as possible; boiling raises the grain on wood or reed splint and makes it fuzzy. It begins to deteriorate.

Tie the dyestuff in cheesecloth and keep it in the pot with the basket materials during the dyeing. This usually makes a stronger dye.

Wet the basket material well before entering it into the dyebath.

If you don't like the results, put the materials through a second or other dyebath.

Reed, raffia, and honeysuckle take dyes best. Birch bark and ash splint usually don't dye as well. Inner cedar bark is naturally brownish red and looks good with most dyes.

    *1. Dyestuff:* Black oak bark *(Quercus* sp.)

             Alice has tried old bark, young bark, twigs, and leaves from trees in her area; all give excellent colors.

      *Ratio:* 4 ounces bark tied in cheesecloth to 5 quarts water and 1/4 teaspoon tin

    *Method:* Boil bark, water, and tin for 30 minutes. Add assorted natural materials. Cover the pot and simmer 15 minutes. Remove the basket materials, rinse, and dry.

      *Color:* On wool—Yellow 83, brilliant Y

*Lightfastness:* L2–3

      *Color:* On raffia—Yellow 82, vivid Y

*Lightfastness:* L2–3

      *Color:* On honeysuckle vine—Brown 61, grayish Br

*Lightfastness:* L2

    *2. Dyestuff:* Madder root *(Rubia tinctorum)*

      *Ratio:* 2 ounces madder root tied in cheesecloth, 3 quarts water, 1/2 teaspoon chrome

    *Method:* Soak the madder root overnight in water. Simmer 1 hour. Add 1/2 teaspoon chrome; stir well to dissolve. Add assorted basket materials. Cover the pot and simmer 45 minutes. Remove the basket materials, rinse, and dry. Note that high temperatures cause the dye to be brown rather than red, red brown, or red orange.

*Color:* On wool—Brown 55, strong Br
*Lightfastness:* L3
*Color:* On raffia—Reddish Brown 43, moderate rBr
*Lightfastness:* L3–4
*Color:* On honeysuckle vine—Reddish Brown 46, grayish rBr
*Lightfastness:* L2–3

*3. Dyestuff:* Black walnut *(Juglans nigra),* green hulls
*Ratio:* A pailful of green hulls
*Method:* Soak hulls in water to cover for a few weeks. Skim off the mold growing on the surface. Strain dye into the dyepot. Add basket material and boil for 1 hour. Remove basket materials, rinse and dry. (Wear rubber gloves to handle the materials.)
*Color:* On honeysuckle vine—Brown 61, grayish Br
*Lightfastness:* L2

*4. Dyestuff:* Onion skins *(Allium* sp.) dye an immediate "antique" basket.
*Ratio:* 1 quart packed onion skins, water to cover, 1/4 teaspoon chrome
*Method:* Put onion skins in pot and cover with water. Boil 45 minutes. Add 1/4 teaspoon chrome and stir to dissolve. Add assorted basket material. Boil 1 hour. Remove basket materials, rinse well, and dry.
*Color:* On wool—Yellow 90, grayish Y
*Lightfastness:* L4
*Color:* On raffia—Yellow 88, dark Y
*Lightfastness:* L3
*Color:* On round reed—Yellow 88, dark Y
*Lightfastness:* L3

# Chapter 5.
# Dyeing
# with Children

## *Stephanie Morris* | New York

Stephanie Morris is a handspinner and dyer; she is also a mother of young children. And the fortunate children with whom she has contact near her New York home are learning about the traditional methods of making and dyeing yarn. Stephanie shares her interest in fibers and dyes through classes and demonstrations at local museums and schools, and she usually has an ongoing class of several middle-grade students who work with her once a week in pursuit of fine yarns and gorgeous colors from natural dyes. Her own dyeing involves a lot of experimentation with various local plants as well as with purchased dyestuffs.

Here are two of Stephanie's ideas for classroom dyeing that are safe, easy, and fun for even very young children—as well as for adults working with them.

### Cold-Water Experimental Dyeing

In classroom situations where it is not possible to use hot dyes, teachers and students may experiment with cold-water dyes. The yarns are not truly dyed and are never rinsed. They do take certain colors well, and the exercise is excellent for demonstration purposes. Additionally, each child can "dye" his or her own yarns in a safe and controlled situation, which is extremely important when working with young children.

Give each child six 8-inch strands of white wool, or one for each

158

dyebath, plus a couple of paper towels. Have the children line up before a table set with cold dyes (in open bowls) and a vinegar/water solution which helps to set the color. Each child places all his or her strands in the bowl with the vinegar/water solution for a few seconds or minutes (time is variable). The yarn is removed and shaken lightly before it is placed on a paper towel. The child then places one strand of yarn in each dyebath for 30 seconds or so (until it "takes" the color). Each strand of yarn is removed from the dyebath and air-dried on a paper towel.

Not all dyes take to this procedure readily, and the teacher will have to test and prepare the dyebaths in advance, either with or without student assistance. Some good dyes to use for this project are red beets, black walnut hulls, and madder root. The colors are different in appearance than they would be if the yarns had been dyed in a normal hot-dyeing situation, and they usually are not fast.

## *Naturally Dyed Eggs*

This is a good project for the classroom as well as for the home. In the United States Easter eggs were dyed with natural dyes during the colonial and post-colonial eras. Since spring rituals with eggs are thousands of years old, people have been dyeing eggs a very long time.

Here's one way to dye eggs using natural materials:

1. Scrub each hard-boiled egg with soap. This is very important—the chicken leaves a protective residue on the shell when the egg is laid, and egg producers sometimes dip freshly laid eggs in a waxy solution to help preserve them.

2. Place the egg in the middle of a square of cheesecloth, and place pieces of natural material around it—onion skins, spinach leaves, flower petals, tree leaves, or whatever you can collect.

3. Wrap the cheesecloth tightly around the egg and tie it with a wire or string. If you do this in a classroom situation, attach a tag or marker with the name of the child who is dyeing the egg.

4. Put water in a pot. Add 1 tablespoon of vinegar per quart of water, place the eggs in the water, and simmer for about 30 minutes.

5. Drain off the water, unwrap the eggs, and admire the natural colors on natural eggs. Children are very intrigued by the process and pleased with the result. Waxed names or designs on these eggs will usually boil off in the hot-water bath to leave a residue on the pot, so this is not suggested as a means of marking the eggs. Lead pencil markings will usually remain well, as will marks made by laundry markers or indelible felt pens.

## Other Projects

In addition to Stephanie's projects, an upper-elementary classroom group would enjoy such things as designing a solar oven and doing solar dyeing and mordanting using fiber, yarns, and fabrics as discussed in Part Two.

Junior high, high school, and college students in chemistry, botany, and other natural-science courses often profit from extended periods of natural dyeing in the curriculum. Weights and liquid measuring, use of equipment, dry measures, scientific investigative procedures, plant identification, ecology, and use of the environment are but a few areas which can be covered in a unit on natural dyes. It is a perfect topic for classes in environmental education.

An enjoyable project for these older students is the "bundle dye." Here's how to do it:

1. Pre-mordant a piece of fabric (1–2 square feet or larger—preferably wool for ease of dyeing, but silk and cotton are all right, too) by a method previously discussed.
2. Lay the wet fabric out flat on a table.
3. Arrange a selection of dyestuffs on the cloth—you can use marigolds, onion skins, cochineal, poplar leaves, or other reliable materials.
4. Fold or roll the fabric, keeping the dyestuff in place as much as possible.
5. Tie the bundle with wool yarn or cotton thread.
6. Put the bundle in a pot with enough water to cover the dyestuff completely.
7. Put a lid on the pot, bring the water to a simmer, and maintain the heat for 1 hour.
8. Cool the bath, bundle in, until you can handle the bundle wearing rubber gloves.
9. Remove the bundle, unwrap it, and remove the dyestuff.
10. Rinse the fabric well and dry.

By including small skeins of yarn with the dyestuff inside the bundle, you can provide enough dyed yarn to do a natural stitchery on your naturally dyed fabric. The fabric will be differently colored where the different dyestuffs were arranged. The serendipitous colors are always a delightful surprise, and at times the cloth will have a mottled or shaded appearance in areas where dyestuff did not make direct contact, or where dyestuffs overlapped.

# Chapter 6.
# Resist Dyeing

## Ikat Dyeing

Ikat dyeing is an ancient tradition first practiced in the Far East. It is basically a resist dyeing technique used on threads before they are woven. Areas of the threads are tied tightly with string, raffia, or plastic; where they are covered with the resist tying, no dyeing will take place. The tied areas resist the dye. After the threads are dyed, they are woven. The resist areas will be the color of the original thread, while the dyed areas will produce a dyed fabric. Where resist areas meet dyed areas in the fabric, a watery appearance is often seen; an image which is not exact—but there nonetheless—will appear if the threads were

*In weft-ikat dyeing, the weft threads are stretched on a frame and tied according to a pre-sketched cartoon. The tied areas will resist the dye, and they will produce the design on the woven cloth.*

tied to match a pattern. Where resist threads weave across other resist areas, a definite pattern may be seen. Since the threads are dyed prior to weaving, it is possible to graph or draw out the pattern one wishes to weave and transfer this to the warp and/or weft threads by tying off the areas meant to remain the original color of the thread—that is, the areas of the resist.

Perhaps the best ikat weaving, or at least the most exact form of this type of dyeing, was done in Japan. It is known as *kasuri* or *e-kasuri* ikat. The *kasuri* patterns form tiny checks or bold linear or geometric

*Japanese* e-kasuri, *or pictorial ikat, dyed with indigo on cotton. This carp was probably dyed and woven in the late 1800s.*

patterns; the *e-kasuri* are more complex and actually produce pictures after the resist-dyed threads are woven. Turtles, birds, and fish are the most popular *e-kasuri* designs.

The tying and dyeing of the warp and weft for ikat weaving is an exact and time-consuming activity. Perhaps because of this it is not the predominating type of dyeing done by most natural dyers. There are, however, dedicated weavers and dyers who very much appreciate the techniques and the results, and who are willing to spend the time and energy to create finely designed, tied, and woven ikat textiles. Traditionally vat dyes, and especially indigo, were used for ikat dyeing. Today, however, dyers and weavers utilize yarns of many sizes dyed with many materials by many methods to produce ikat fabrics or other articles utilizing tightly bound resist-dyed yarns. Fabrics may also be tied and dyed, though they demand slightly different techniques to prepare them for the dyepot.

162

# Tie-Dye and Related Dye-Resist Techniques on Fabric

Perhaps the two most popular methods for resist-dyeing fabrics are known as batik and tie-dye. While dyers have their own favorite working methods, there are some basic procedures that can be followed to give good results.

Batik dyeing is usually done on flat fabric using wax as the resistant material. Where hot wax is applied to the ground of the fabric, it coats the fibers and will not allow dye to penetrate and color the cloth. Since the majority of natural dyeing is done with simmering or at least hot water baths, and since wax softens and comes off the fiber in hot water or in heat in general, using wax for resist areas is not satisfactory. It can be used as the resist on cloth to be dipped into cold dyes such as indigo vats, however, and will give excellent results.

It is possible to utilize some rather new chemical compounds that, when applied to fabric, do not get hard and resistant until they are heated. It is also possible to paint onto the fabric with a heat-resistant paint or shellac; this will resist the dye and also become a part of the background pattern on the fabric. There are many possibilities for utilizing batik techniques with natural dyes, but the dyer must bear in mind the peculiarities of the fabrics, dyes, and resist materials with which he or she is working.

Some dyers have experimented with serigraphy (silk screen) and natural dyes, and have found that the dyes must be thickened in order to be screened onto the fabric. Additionally, the fabric must be pre-mordanted, and in most cases wet and warm before the dye will take during the screen process. Certain areas of the Far East—Okinawa, for example—were involved in production of stenciled fabrics in which indigo or other dyes were stenciled directly onto cotton fabrics. Sometimes the dyes were actually painted onto the fabrics, or used with rice-paste resists to keep natural areas.

Perhaps the easiest and most successful resist dyeing of fabrics will be done by the tie-dye or stitch-and-dye techniques that are still employed by peoples all over the world. The techniques are simple and effective, and they can be used with any natural dye procedures on natural fabrics. These tie-dyed fabrics are sometimes referred to as *plangi,* which is the Indonesian term used to describe resist-dyed fabrics. Sewing techniques such as the African *tritik* or Japanese *shibori* (which also involves tying) are easily done, but they are time-consuming if done with the traditional tiny stitches.

163

Intricate designs are possible to obtain; they will be determined by the size of the ties or stitches and the planned pattern. Fine wools and silks work quite well with most natural dyes. Do try cotton with indigo and any other dyes that you find will successfully dye the cotton fabric, as it is much less expensive than either fine wool challis or flannel or silk. Viscose rayon will also work well with resist techniques.

*A TIE-DYED SCARF: Here's the white silk scarf just as it was received from the manufacturer.*

*The first ties are done with Japanese plastic resist tape. Running stitches in rows can be pulled tight to leave fine rows of dots after dyeing is completed.*

The accompanying photographs, here and on the next three pages, demonstrate some tie-dyeing and stitching done on silk. You may also obtain good results by folding and clamping the fabrics, or rolling and tying, or tying the fabrics back on themselves (a tight knot will resist the dye, but it may be difficult to untie once the fabric has been dyed and dried). You may wish to dye yarns along with the fabrics in order to have a good match for stitchery or other embellishing of the dyed fabrics.

*The scarf with ties and drawn stitches.*

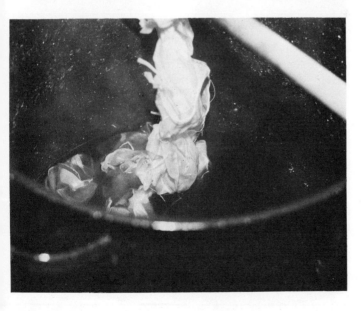

*The scarf is lowered into the first dyebath—a light yellow from sage, with alum in the dyebath.*

165

*The scarf after the first bath and after more wrapping tape is tied over the stitched areas.*

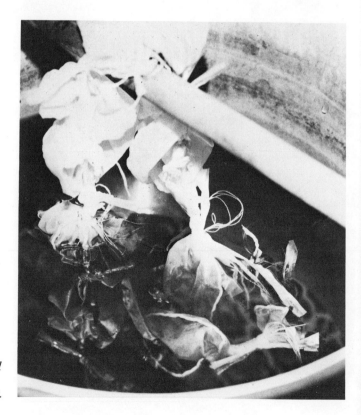

*The sage-dyed scarf now goes into a logwood bath which will overdye the yellow sage dye.*

*The scarf after the logwood dye and removal of ties and stitches. Many wrinkles set into the silk during the dyeing. Most can be pressed out if the silk is ironed while wet with an iron set to press wool.*

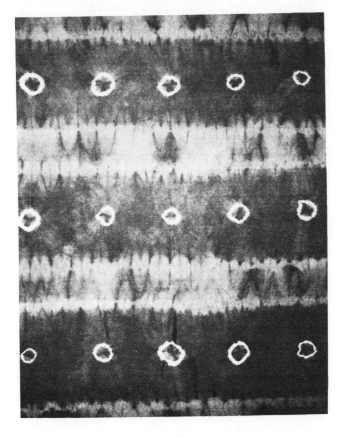

*An elegant length of silk yardage dyed by the author using a weak black-walnut dye overdyed with logwood. The white circles are resisted and free of all dye. The zigzag bars are a light cocoa brown, and the body is a rich purplish brown.*

167

# Appendix A.

## *Mass (Weight): Ounces to Grams and Grams to Ounces, Etc.*

| ounces (oz.) | = | 28 grams (g) |
| pounds (lb.) | = | 0.45 kilograms (kg) |
| grams (g) | = | 0.035 ounces (oz.) |
| kilograms (kg) | = | 2.2 pounds (lb.) |

## *Volume: Milliliters to Ounces to Grams to Cups, Etc.*

| milliliters (mL) | = | 0.03 fluid ounces (fl. oz.) |
| liters (L) | = | 2.1 pints (pt.) |
| liters (L) | = | 1.06 quarts (qt.) |
| liters (L) | = | 0.26 gallons (gal.) |
| teaspoons (tsp.) | = | 5 milliliters (mL) |
| tablespoons (tbsp.) | = | 15 milliliters (mL) |
| fluid ounces (fl. oz.) | = | 30 milliliters (mL) |
| cups (c.) | = | 0.24 liters (L) |
| pints (pt.) | = | 0.47 liters (L) |
| quarts (qt.) | = | 0.95 liters (L) |
| gallons (gal.) | = | 3.8 liters (L) |

## *Temperature: Fahrenheit to Celsius and Back Again*

To convert Fahrenheit (F) into Celsius (C)—subtract 32, multiply by 5, divide by 9.

To convert Celsius (C) into Fahrenheit (F)—multiply by 9, divide by 5, then add 32.

0° C = 32° F (the freezing point of water at sea level)
100° C = 212° F (the boiling point of water at sea level)

# Appendix B.

American Association of Textile Chemists and Colorists
P.O. Box 12215
Research Triangle Park, N.C. 27709

National Bureau of Standards
Washington, D.C. 20234

Office of Standard Reference Materials
Chemistry B311
Washington, D.C. 20234
•Color Kit #SRM 2107 includes the Centroid Color Charts along with the Dictionary of Color Names. #SRM 2106 contains the Centroid Color Charts without the reference handbook.

The Wool Bureau, Inc.
Technical Services Center
225 Crossways Park Drive
Woodbury, Long Island, N.Y. 11797

# Appendix C.

Alliance Import Company
1021 "R" Street
Sacramento, Calif. 95814
•Wide selection of imported dyestuffs, wholesale and retail. Send stamped, self-addressed envelope for information.

The Arachnid
P.O. Box 1355
Ormond Beach, Fla. 32074
•Imported dyestuffs and information and publications. Send stamped, self-addressed envelope for information.

Blessing Historical Foundation
P.O. Box 517
Blessing, Tex. 77419
•Madder seeds are their specialty.

Cerulean Blue, Ltd.
P.O. Box 5126
1314 N.E. 43rd Street
Seattle, Wash. 98105
•Wide selection of equipment, dyestuffs, mordants, fabrics. Write for free catalog.

Dharma Trading Company
P.O. Box 916
1952 University Avenue
Berkeley, Calif. 94704
•Wide selection of equipment, dyestuffs, mordants, fibers, yarns, and fabrics. Catalog available.

Gordons' Naturals
P.O. Box 506
Roseburg, Ore. 97470
•Fibers, dyestuffs, mordants, equipment. Catalog available.

Hybrid Press
P.O. Box 276
Pleasanton, Calif. 94566
•California native dyestuff, selected naturally dyed yarns. Send stamped, self-addressed envelope.

Jones Sheep Farm
R.R. 2
Peabody, Kans. 66866
•Unspun wool fleece, instruction, publications. Send stamped, self-addressed envelope.

Kasuri Dyeworks
1959 Shattuck Avenue
Berkeley, Calif. 94704
•Traditional Japanese dyeing equipment, fabrics, dyestuffs, mordants, resist materials. Catalog 50¢.

Cheryl Kolander Silks
276 North Myrtle
Myrtle Creek, Ore. 97457
•Wide selection of natural and naturally dyed silk threads/yarns. Catalog and generous samples, $5.00.

Designs by Parsons
8402 E. Mangun Road
Mesa, Ariz. 85207
•Wide selection of mordants and traditional dyestuffs. Send stamped, self-addressed envelope.

Straw Into Gold
5550 College Avenue
Oakland, Calif. 94618
•Wide selection of fibers, yarns, mordants, dyestuffs, equipment. Catalog $1.00.

WoodsEdge Farmstead
P.O. Box 464
Laurel Avenue
Kingston, N.J. 08528
•Wide selection of fibers and spun yarns ready for dyeing, naturally dyed commercial and handspun yarns, mordants and dyestuffs. Catalog 75¢.

# Index